LEAVING CERTIFICATE

LESS STRESS
MORE
SUCCESS

Chemistry Revision

Eamonn Healy

Gill & Macmillan

Gill & Macmillan

Hume Avenue

Park West

Dublin 12

with associated companies throughout the world

www.gillmacmillan.ie

978 07171 4703 8

Design by Liz White Designs

Artwork and print origination by MPS Limited, a Macmillan Company

The paper used in this book is made from the wood pulp of managed forests.
For every tree felled, at least one tree is planted, thereby renewing natural resources.

For permission to reproduce photographs, the author and publisher gratefully acknowledge the following:

© Alamy: 54; © Mary Evans Picture Library: 1, 3, 4, 10; © Science Photo Library: 5, 11, 46, 47, 53, 55; © Topfoto: 56.

The authors and publisher have made every effort to trace all copyright holders, but if any has been inadvertently overlooked we would be pleased to make the necessary arrangement at the first opportunity.

CONTENTS

HL

Introduction

Exam paper analysis

The following description is applicable to Higher and Ordinary level students except for a few minor points which are highlighted.

 Note: Material that is to be studied only by those taking Higher level is indicated in the text.

Structure of exam and advice on core questions

- There are 11 questions on the exam paper and eight must be attempted. Each question carries 50 marks.
- There are two sections to the paper:

Section A

- In Section A there are three questions based on the mandatory experiments. At least two of these questions must be attempted.
- In Section A it is imperative that you cover in detail:

Question 1

This is generally based on all the titrations on your course. All the titrations are located in Chapters 8, 9 and 10 in this book to facilitate easy access and revision.

Ordinary level candidates have only to cover three of these titrations and these titrations are located in Chapter 8.

Question 2

This is generally based on the eight organic experiments on the course. This question is comprehensively covered in Chapters 16 and 17 in this book.

Note: in the case of the ordinary level paper, question 1 is generally based on organic experiments and question 2 is based on titrations.

Question 3

Question 3 in this section is based on the remaining mandatory experiments.

Section B

- In Section B there are eight questions, five of which must be answered.

Question 4

In this question eight short questions out of 11 must be attempted. It is recommended that you attempt all 11 of these short questions (if possible) as you will be given merit for the best eight. Each short question merits 6 marks.

These questions cover the whole course so it is essential that all the key definitions on the course be learned with the utmost precision and accuracy. These key points are highlighted in each chapter in this book. The following example demonstrates the level of accuracy required in answering these short questions.

Sample short question: State Charles's law (6 marks).

Solution

At constant pressure the volume of a fixed mass of any gas (3 marks) varies directly with the *absolute (Kelvin)* temperature (3 marks).

If a candidate just stated 'temperature' instead of 'absolute temperature' 3 marks would be deducted.

Question 5

This question covers atomic theory and the periodic table, bonding and related topics such as shapes of molecules. It is covered in Chapters 1 to 5 (inclusive) in this book.

Question 6

This question is generally based on the organic chemistry and fuels section of the course. The organic chemistry section also features as a separate question in questions 7, 8 or 9.

Therefore it is crucial that the organic chemistry section be the core part of study for the Leaving Certificate exam as there can be up to three questions on this subject on the paper. The organic chemistry and fuels section is covered in Chapters 13, 14 and 15 for easy access.

Questions 7, 8 and 9

One of these questions is given over to organic chemistry as already noted. The other two questions vary in content but generally feature questions from:
(a) Water, acid-base theory and pH
(b) Rates and equilibrium.

Questions 10 and 11

Both of these questions have an internal choice where two parts out of three must be answered. These questions vary in content but often feature questions on stoichiometry, electrochemistry and gas laws.

Question 11(c) features the options on the course.

Note:

- Higher level students must cover in their entirety either option 1 or option 2.
- Ordinary level students must study one option from 1A, 1B, 2A or 2B.

Timing for the exam

- There are three hours in total to do the exam.
- Allow ten minutes for reading and choosing questions.
- Then allow a limit of 20 minutes for each of the eight questions.
- Allow ten minutes at the end of the exam for re-reading and checking your answers.

Exam strategy

- It is important to attempt all eight questions as required.
- It is important to choose questions carefully. Always read a question in full before deciding to do it as there may be parts which carry a lot of marks that you may struggle to answer well enough.
- When doing a calculation make sure to show all the steps as there are marks allocated for each step. There is a tendency when using a calculator to do the whole calculation on it and write the final answer down. This is a mistake as if this final answer is wrong all the marks will be lost (see sample answer on next page).
- Always draw a diagram to illustrate an answer even if it is not specifically asked for in the question. Valuable marks can be gained from a diagram if a certain point is missing from the written description.
- Pay close attention to the marking scheme for a question which is written on the paper. Remember that questions are generally marked in units of three so if there are 12 marks allocated to a question four points are generally required in the answer.
- Only attempt an extra question if you have checked all your other eight questions and are satisfied that you cannot improve on them.
- Read carefully the sample questions and answers which are given in this textbook to see how questions should be answered and the level of detail required.
- The Leaving Certificate chemistry exam generally comes towards the end of the exam schedule. It is important, therefore, to use the time before the exam wisely as a lot of the course material will be forgotten at that stage with revision of other subjects.
- It is important in the days before the exam to concentrate on the memory intensive areas of your course such as the organic section and also to revise key definitions in each section.
- At that point you will take great comfort in the fact that you have this book to maximise your revision time and indeed maximise your scoring potential!! I wish you every success.

Sample exam question: 2005 Q8
Higher level

Q8 (a) Define (i) acid (ii) base according to the Bronsted–Lowry theory. (8 marks)

(b) Identify one species acting as an acid, and identify its conjugate base in the
following system: H_2F^+ + Cl^- $\rightleftharpoons$ HCl + HF   (6 marks)

(c) Calculate the pH of a 0.002 M solution of methanoic acid. The value of K_a
for methanoic acid is 1.8×10^{-4}.   (12 marks)

(d) What is meant by biochemical oxygen demand (BOD) of a water
sample?   (6 marks)

(e) Describe clearly the processes involved in the primary and secondary
stages of urban sewage treatment. What substances are removed in the
tertiary treatment?   (18 marks)

Solution

(a) Define (i) acid: proton (hydrogen ion, H^+) donor   (4)
(ii) base: proton (hydrogen ion, H^+) acceptor   (4)

(b) acid = H_2F^+ (3) conjugate base = HF   (3)
or   acid = HCL (3)   conjugate base = Cl^- (3)

Note: if the candidate does not state which is the acid or conjugate base, the order
in the question is taken as the intended order.

(c) $pH = -\log\sqrt{K_a \times M}$ (3)

$pH = -\log\sqrt{1.8 \times 10^{-4} \times 0.002}$ (3)
$pH = 3.22$ (6)

Note that the above shows that each step in the calculation merits 3 marks.
Therefore it demonstrates the importance of writing every step down.

(d) BOD: oxygen consumed (3) when a sample of water kept in the dark at 20 °C for
5 days.   Screening (metal screens)   (3)

Note the precise detail of the test required in the answer.

(e) Describe: primary treatment: physical/removal of solids (large particles, leaves,
twigs)   Screening (metal screens)   (2 × 3)

secondary: oxidation/use of air or oxygen (3) by microorganisms (bacteria,
biological)   (3)

What is present in tertiary?   Nitrates (nitrogen compounds)   (3)
Phosphates (phosphorus compounds)   (3)

Note the presence of a solidus (/) here indicates alternative answers.

List of mandatory experiments

HL

1 Atomic Structure

aims To revise the following:
- Dalton's atomic theory
- Thomson's 'plum pudding' theory
- Discovery of electron, nucleus, proton and neutron
- Isotopes and relative atomic mass
- Elements and the periodic table of elements

John Dalton's atomic theory (1808)

1. All matter is made up of **very small identical particles called atoms**.
2. **All atoms are indivisible and cannot be broken down into simpler particles**.
3. **Atoms cannot be created or destroyed**.

This simple theory, **that an atom was indivisible**, was replaced with the discovery **of subatomic particles** due to various experiments carried out in the nineteenth century.

John Dalton

Discovery of cathode rays by William Crookes

- Crookes examined what happened when an electric current was passed through a glass vacuum tube as in the diagram.
- He showed the **existence of cathode rays i.e. streams of charged particles coming from the negative electrode or cathode**.
- When an object such as a Maltese cross was placed in the path of the rays a shadow was cast at the far end of the tube.

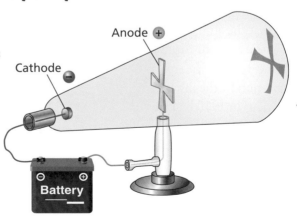

Crookes' apparatus

Discovery of the electron by J.J. Thomson

- In 1897 an English scientist called **J.J. Thomson**, using a more sophisticated vacuum tube, discovered that the cathode rays of Crookes' experiment could be attracted to a positive plate. This proved that **they were negative**.
- **They were called electrons**, a name that had previously been proposed by George Stoney, an Irish scientist.
- Thomson also calculated $\dfrac{e}{m}$ (the **charge to mass ratio**) of the electron.

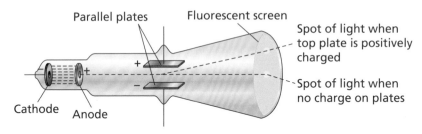

Parallel plates   Fluorescent screen

Spot of light when top plate is positively charged

Spot of light when no charge on plates

Cathode   Anode

Thomson's cathode ray tube

Millikan's oil drop experiment: to measure the charge on an electron

A later experiment by **Robert Millikan** called 'Millikan's oil drop experiment' enabled the **charge of an electron** to be calculated. Therefore, the **mass of an electron could also be calculated as the charge to mass ratio had been calculated earlier by Thomson.**

Thomson's 'plum pudding' model of the atom

In this theory, Thomson proposed that the **atom was a sphere which has a positive charge with negative electrons embedded in it at random** so that the atom would be electrically neutral as in the diagram.

However, this theory was called into question by the discovery of the nucleus in 1910 by Ernest Rutherford and his research team.

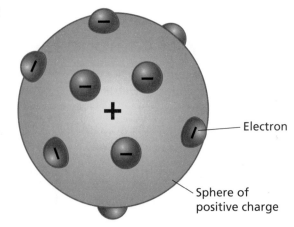

Electron

Sphere of positive charge

Thomson's 'plum pudding' model of the atom

Discovery of the nucleus by Rutherford

Rutherford and his team bombarded very thin sheets of gold foil with positive particles called alpha particles. Alpha particles are helium nuclei with a double positive charge.

Alpha particle: $^{4}_{2}He^{2+}$

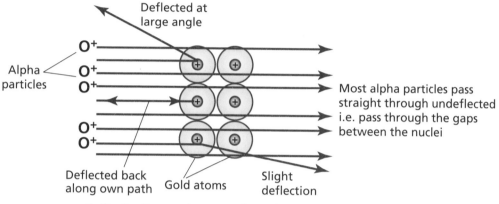

Rutherford's experiment to show the existence of a nucleus

Three main results were found:

1. The majority of the alpha particles passed through the gold foil. This proved that the atom was mainly empty space.
2. Some alpha particles were deflected as they were repelled by the positive charge of the nucleus.
3. Other particles rebounded back along their own path as they hit the nucleus.

Rutherford's explanation of the results

- **Rutherford** explained the above experiment by proposing that the **centre of the atom consisted of a small, dense, highly positive body called the nucleus**.
- The nucleus was very small in comparison with the atom as a whole. This explained why most of the particles passed through while only a small number were deflected.

Ernest Rutherford

Discovery of the proton by Rutherford

- **Rutherford** and his research team (Geiger and Marsden) bombarded various substances with alpha particles.
- They found that in the case of the smaller atoms like oxygen and nitrogen **small positive particles were being released. Rutherford called these particles protons**.
- This did not happen in the case of the larger atoms because the nucleus had a much stronger repelling effect due to a stronger positive charge.

Discovery of the neutron by Chadwick

In his experiment in 1932 Chadwick bombarded beryllium with alpha particles. He found that **neutral particles were being emitted from the nucleus. These had the same mass as the proton and he called them neutrons**.

This was a tremendous discovery at the time as neutrons were later used to split atoms of uranium and release energy in nuclear reactors and the atomic bomb.

James Chadwick

History of the periodic table of elements

The ancient Greek philosophers believed that there were four basic elements – **earth, air, water and fire** – and all substances were arrangements of these.

Robert Boyle: defining the element

The Greeks' idea of an element was substantially improved by the Irish scientist Robert Boyle.

key definition

An element is a substance that cannot be split into simpler substances by chemical means. For example, carbon consists only of carbon atoms.

Humphrey Davy: isolating elements by electrolysis

- After it was discovered that water could be split up by electricity into hydrogen and oxygen, a scientist called **Humphrey Davy** concluded that it should be possible to break down other substances by the same method.

- In 1807 he discovered **potassium** by passing electricity through a sample of melted potassium hydroxide (KOH). In the experiment, tiny globules of potassium caught fire, giving off a purple flame.
- Three days later, again by electrolysis, Davy isolated **sodium** from a melted sample of sodium hydroxide.
- Davy also discovered **calcium, magnesium, strontium and barium**.

Johann Dobereiner: Law of triads

Johann Dobereiner (1819) was the first to establish a relationship between the properties of elements and their atomic weights.

- He looked at groups of three elements called triads, for example **chlorine (Cl), bromine (Br) and iodine (I)** and showed that they had similar chemical properties. He also showed that the atomic weight of the middle element i.e. bromine is midway between the other two.
- Another example of a triad was lithium (Li), sodium (Na) and potassium (K). However, only a few examples of triads could be found.

Newlands: Law of octaves

- In 1864 an English scientist called John Newlands proposed his Law of octaves where he stated that **properties of elements repeat every eighth element when the elements are listed in order of their atomic weights**.
- Newlands drew up a table containing all the known elements at the time in order of increasing atomic weights.
- Discrepancies occurred in his table due to the fact that many elements had not been discovered at the time (in fact his theory only worked for the first 16 elements). He should have left gaps for undiscovered elements instead of incorrectly trying to make elements fit the pattern.

Mendeleev's periodic table

- A Russian scientist called Mendeleev improved on the work of Newlands by constructing a **table of elements where the elements were ordered in terms of atomic weight** and gaps were left for undiscovered elements.
- However, in a few cases, he had to reverse the order of elements to make them fit into groups with similar properties. For example he had to place iodine before tellurium even though the atomic weight of iodine is greater than tellurium.
- Mendeleev proposed his periodic law: when elements are arranged in order of their atomic weight, properties of the elements repeat periodically.

Dmitri Mendeleev

Moseley and the modern periodic table

In 1913, using X-rays, Moseley was able to determine the number of protons in an atom of an element and this number is called the atomic number. **If elements were now placed in order of atomic number rather than atomic weight, elements fell naturally into their correct groups, unlike Mendeleev's table.**

Differences between the modern table and Mendeleev's table

Mendeleev's table	Modern table
1. Elements are ordered in terms of atomic weight	1. Elements are ordered in terms of atomic number
2. Less elements e.g. Group O elements missing	2. More elements e.g. Group O elements present
3. Gaps left for undiscovered elements	3. No gaps

Properties of electrons, protons and neutrons

The properties of the three subatomic particles are compared in the following table.

Particle	Relative mass	Relative charge	Location
Electron	1/1836	−1	Orbits nucleus
Proton	1	+1	In nucleus
Neutron	1	0	In nucleus

Atomic number (Z)

key
definition

The atomic number of an atom is the number of protons in the nucleus.

In a neutral atom the number of protons is equal to the number of electrons. The atomic number is given the symbol **Z** and gives an element its position in the periodic table.

Mass number (A)

The mass number is the number of protons and neutrons in the nucleus of an atom.

The mass number is given the symbol **A**. It is important to note that the number of neutrons is found by subtracting the atomic number from the **mass number (A–Z)**. As the electrons in an atom have very little mass, the mass of an atom is in effect the mass of the protons and neutrons i.e. the mass of the nucleus.

Calculating numbers of protons, neutrons and electrons

Example

Find the number of (i) protons (ii) neutrons and (iii) electrons in:

$$_{28}^{58}Ni^{2+} \quad \text{ion?}$$

Number of protons = 28 (smaller number is the atomic)

Number of neutrons = 58 − 28 = 30 neutrons

Number of electrons = 28 − 2 = 26 electrons

In a **neutral atom** the number of electrons is the same as the number of protons. The atom in the above example has **lost two electrons and thus has a double positive charge**. Also note that the mass number and atomic number are given in the reverse order to the way they appear in the tables.

Isotopes

Isotopes are atoms with the same number of protons and different numbers of neutrons.

Example

Neon has two isotopes

(i) $_{10}^{20}Ne$ and   (ii) $_{10}^{22}Ne$

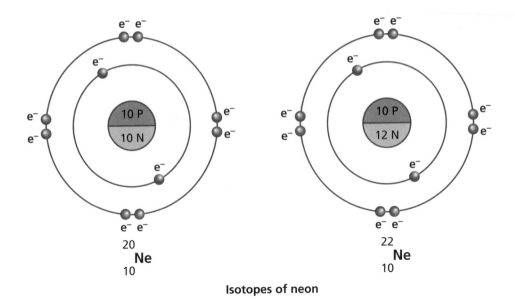

Isotopes of neon

In isotope (i) Ne has 10 protons and 10 neutrons (20 – 10)
In isotope (ii) Ne has 10 protons but 12 neutrons (22 – 10)

Relative atomic mass

key definition

The relative atomic mass is the average mass of an atom of an element, as it occurs in nature, compared with one-twelfth the mass of the carbon-12 isotope.

An instrument called a **mass spectrometer** is used to measure the relative atomic mass of an element.

This mass spectrometer can measure:

(i) **the number of isotopes of an element**

(ii) **the relative abundance of each isotope.**

From these figures the relative atomic mass of an atom of that element can be calculated. This is illustrated in the example on the next page.

Sample exam question: 2006 Q10(a) Higher level HL

**Calculate the relative atomic mass of a sample of lithium given that the mass
spectrometer shows it consists of 7.4% of ^{6}Li and 92.6% of ^{7}Li.**   (6 marks)

Solution

A 100 atom sample of lithium contains 92.6 of lithium-7 and 7.4 lithium-6 atoms.

$$92.6 \times 7 = 648.2$$
$$7.4 \times 6 = \underline{44.4}$$

mass of 100 atom = 692.6   (3 marks)

mass of one atom = 6.926

Relative atomic mass of lithium = 6.926   (3 marks)

In the above example 6.93 would be accepted as an answer for full marks.

exam focus

Since relative atomic mass is the average of the mass numbers of the isotopes of an
element, it will not be a whole number.

2 Radioactivity

aims To revise the following:

- Discovery of radioactivity
- Types of radiation
- Radioisotopes and their uses
- Half-life
- Comparison of nuclear and chemical reactions

Becquerel discovers radioactivity

- Henri Becquerel is credited with the discovery of radioactivity.
- By chance he left some uranium salts resting on a photographic plate and wrapped them in black paper. To his surprise the photographic plate became darkened in the area near the uranium salts.
- He correctly concluded that the uranium salts were giving off radiation. He went on to show that this radiation was spontaneous i.e. was given off naturally and was not induced by factors such as light and heat.

key definition

Radioactivity is defined as the spontaneous breakdown of unstable nuclei with the release of one or more types of radiation.

Henri Becquerel

Discovery of polonium and radium by the Curies

Two of Becquerel's colleagues, Pierre and Marie Curie, further investigated the release of radioactivity from uranium salts in pitchblende. They successfully isolated two other radioactive elements, namely polonium and radium.

They named polonium after their native Poland and the other element radium means 'giver of rays'. The Curies shared the Nobel Prize for Physics in 1903 with Becquerel for their work on radioactivity.

Pierre and Marie Curie

Types of radiation

About ten years after Becquerel discovered radioactivity, scientists had isolated three types of radiation i.e. alpha, beta and gamma radiation. The different properties of these three types of radiation are given in the following table.

Radiation type	Alpha (α)	Beta (β)	Gamma (γ)
Nature of radiation	Helium nuclei ($_2^4He^{2+}$)	Electrons	Waves of high energy
Charge	+2	−1	No charge
Penetrating power	Weak penetration (stopped by paper)	Medium penetration (stopped by 5 mm of aluminium)	Strong penetration (stopped by several cm of lead)

This diagram is a summary of penetrating power.

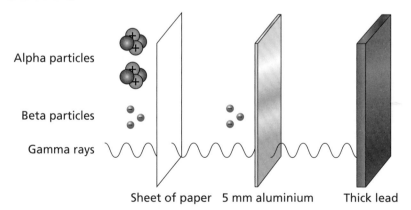

Alpha particles

Beta particles

Gamma rays

Sheet of paper   5 mm aluminium   Thick lead

The relative penetrating power of alpha, beta and gamma radiation
Gamma > beta > alpha radiation

Effect of alpha particle emission

Alpha particles are helium nuclei and may be represented as $^4_2He^{2+}$.

When an atom loses an alpha particle from the nucleus, its atomic number decreases by two and its mass number decreases by 4.

Example of alpha particle emission

$$^{214}_{84}Po \longrightarrow \ ^4_2He \ + \ ^{210}_{82}Pb$$

polonium   alpha   lead

Alpha particles can be hazardous to health and exposure to alpha radiation can lead to cancer.

Everyday use of alpha particle emission

An everyday example of an alpha emitter is Americium–241 which is used in smoke detectors. Radiation from smoke detectors does not present a health hazard in the home as alpha particles produced are not very penetrating. The americium in smoke detectors does not need to be replaced as it has a long half-life (this is the time taken for half of the nuclei in a given sample to decay) of over 400 years.

Effect of beta particle emission

A beta particle is an electron with a negative charge and greater penetrating ability than an alpha particle.

A beta particle is an electron which is emitted from the nucleus when a neutron breaks up into a proton and an electron. The proton remains in the nucleus and therefore the atomic number increases by one. There is no change in mass as the electron has negligible mass.

Example of beta particle emission:

$$^{14}_6C \longrightarrow \ ^{\ 0}_{-1}e \ + \ ^{14}_7N$$

carbon   beta   nitrogen

The atomic number increases by one in beta particle emission which means that carbon is changed into nitrogen.

Everyday use of beta particle emission

Carbon dating

- Two of the isotopes of carbon are carbon–12 and carbon–14. Carbon–14 is a radioactive isotope but carbon–12 is not radioactive.
- Carbon-14 releases beta particles and has a long half-life of 5700 years.
- When a plant or animal is living, the ratio of C^{14} to C^{12} is constant. When a plant or animal dies, the unstable C^{14} starts to decay but C^{12} stays unchanged. Therefore, the ratio of C^{14} to C^{12} changes.
- By measuring the changed ratio and using the half-life, scientists can determine the age of a specimen. This is called carbon dating.

A radioisotope is an isotope of an element that emits radiation, e.g. carbon–14 emits beta particles.

Effect of gamma ray emission

Gamma rays are high energy electromagnetic radiation. They are not particles and are usually released in conjunction with either alpha or beta particles.

When gamma rays are released from the nucleus there is no change in the structure of the nucleus. The element does not change as only energy is being released.

When an alpha or beta particle is lost from an atom of an element, the element changes into another element. This is called **transmutation**. However when a gamma ray is emitted the element does not change.

Everyday use of gamma ray emission

An example of a gamma emitter is cobalt-60 which is used in cancer treatment and to preserve food. Cobalt-60 releases gamma rays according to the following equation:

$$^{60}_{27}Co \longrightarrow ^{60}_{27}Co + \gamma$$

Cobalt-60   Cobalt-60   Gamma ray

It is important to note that a new element is not formed in gamma ray release.

Differences between chemical and nuclear reactions

The differences between chemical and nuclear reactions are summarised in the following table.

Chemical reaction	Nuclear reaction
Cannot change one element into another	Elements can be changed into other elements (transmutation)
No change occurs in the nucleus. It involves sharing or transfer of electrons	Change occurs in the nucleus e.g. change in number of protons or neutrons

Half-life of radioisotopes

A radioisotope is an isotope of an element that emits radiation.

The half-life of a radioactive isotope is the time taken for half of the nuclei in a given sample to decay.

Half-lives can vary enormously with the radioisotope. Some can have a half-life of a fraction of a second whereas others can have a half-life of thousands of years.

Specified demonstration experiment: To examine the properties of alpha, beta and gamma radiation

Procedure

- Set up apparatus as shown in diagram.
- The Geiger-Müller tube and counter give an initial reading without bringing a radioactive source near them. This is due to background radiation caused by natural radioactivity e.g. radon.
- Measure and record the average background count per minute.
- Bring an alpha particle source about 4 cm from the window of the Geiger-Müller tube. A count is taken for one minute.

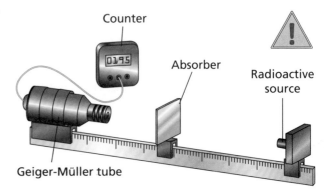

To compare the penetrating power of radioactive particles using a Geiger-Müller tube

- The count is now greater than the background count. Subtract the background count and record the count that is caused by the alpha radiation.
- If a sheet of paper is placed between alpha source and Geiger counter the count returns to the background count. This proves that paper blocks alpha radiation.
- Repeat the experiment using a beta particle source. This time it takes a 3 mm sheet of aluminium to block the beta radiation.
- Again repeat the experiment using a source of gamma radiation.
- This time it takes a 4 cm block of lead to block the gamma radiation.

Conclusion

This demonstration proves that gamma radiation is the most penetrating and alpha radiation is the least penetrating.

Background radiation around us

There is a low level of background radiation around us at all times. Radon gas is the main source of natural radiation. Radon is emitted from rocks in the form of alpha particles. There is a health risk of cancer associated with high levels of radon gas. Therefore radon barriers are being put into buildings to offset this problem.

Other sources of background radiation are cosmic rays from outer space, X-rays, and cobalt-60 in medical treatments.

Sample exam question: 2004 Q11(a) Higher level

(i) Define radioactivity. (6 marks)

(ii) State two properties of beta particles. (6 marks)

(iii) Write an equation for the nuclear reaction involved in the beta decay of ^{14}C (carbon-14). (6 marks)

(iv) Explain how the carbon-14 isotope allows certain archaeological discoveries to be dated. (7 marks)

Solution

(i) Spontaneous emission of radiation (3 marks) by unstable nuclei (3 marks).

(ii) Negative/negligible mass/more penetrating than alpha particles/damage body cells (cause cancer) .... any two (2 × 3 marks)

(iii) $^{14}_{6}C \longrightarrow \ ^{\ \ 0}_{-1}e \ + \ ^{14}_{7}N$ (6 marks)

   carbon   beta   nitrogen

(iv) In living things ratio of carbon-12 to carbon-14 is constant (3 marks). After death decrease in carbon-14 leads to change in ratio with time and using the half-life scientists can determine age of specimen (4 marks).

3 Electronic Structure of the Atom

 aims To revise the following:
- Bohr's model of the atom
- Energy levels in the atom
- Evidence for Bohr's theory
- Absorption spectra
- Modern orbital theory and electronic configuration
- Atomic radii and ionisation energy
- Electronegativity

Niels Bohr

1n 1913, the Danish scientist Niels Bohr put forward his theory of energy levels in an atom. He based his theory on the analysis of emission spectra he obtained when he excited hydrogen atoms in a discharge tube.

Main points of Bohr's theory

1. Electrons can only occupy certain areas within the atom, called energy levels.

 key definition

An energy level is the fixed energy value of an electron in an atom.

2. The ground state of an electron is when it occupies the lowest energy level available to it.

HL
3. When an electron absorbs energy it jumps from a lower energy level to a higher energy level. The electron is now said to be in an 'excited state'. However, the electrons are less stable in higher levels and tend to drop back down again to lower levels.

4. When an electron drops from a higher to a lower level a definite amount of energy is released in the form of light of a particular frequency.

5. The definite amount of energy released when an electron drops from a higher to a lower level is equal to the difference in energy between the two energy levels. This energy difference is given by the equation:

$$E_2 - E_1 = hf$$

where E_2 = energy value of higher level
E_1 = energy value of lower level
h = Planck's constant
f = frequency of light emitted.

6. The energy levels are given a number (n) called the principal quantum number. The lowest energy level is numbered n = 1.

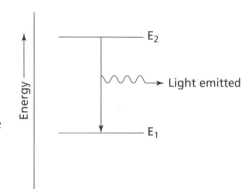

Spectroscopic evidence to support Bohr's theory

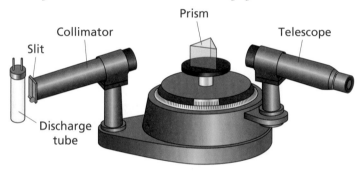

Spectroscope

When a gaseous element such as hydrogen is electrically excited in a discharge tube the electrons of the hydrogen atoms absorb the energy and then give off energy in the form of light.

When this light was examined by a spectroscope as in the diagram, a line spectrum was obtained.

Sample exam question: 2004 Q10(b) Higher level

Describe how Bohr used line emission spectra to explain the existence of energy levels in atoms. (13 marks)

Solution

The line spectrum obtained provided evidence for Bohr's theory in that:

- electrons in the ground state (lowest energy level) (4 marks)
- absorb energy and jump to higher levels (3 marks)
- the light energy released by an electron on dropping back down from a higher to a lower level is of a definite wavelength or frequency (3 marks)
- each line in the spectrum represents a specific jump from a higher to a lower level. Electrons in atoms are allowed only certain jumps from one energy level to another (3 marks).

It was found that the wavelengths of light found in the emission spectrum for hydrogen fell into different sets. One of these sets is called the Balmer series and was discovered by a Swiss physicist Johann Balmer in 1885.

exam focus

> The Balmer series of lines in the visible part of hydrogen spectrum represents jumps from higher levels to the second or n = 2 energy level.

Mandatory experiment: Flame test evidence to support Bohr's theory

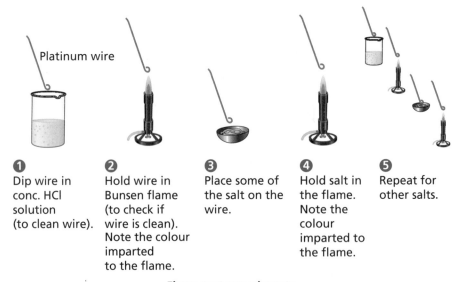

Platinum wire

1 Dip wire in conc. HCl solution (to clean wire).

2 Hold wire in Bunsen flame (to check if wire is clean). Note the colour imparted to the flame.

3 Place some of the salt on the wire.

4 Hold salt in the flame. Note the colour imparted to the flame.

5 Repeat for other salts.

Flame test experiments

Procedure

- Clean a platinum or nichrome wire thoroughly, in a fume cupboard, using concentrated hydrochloric acid.
- Place the wire in a Bunsen flame, making sure it imparts no colour to the flame.
- Dip the wire in a clean sample of hydrochloric acid (HCl) and then into a sample of the salt to be tested.
- Hold the wire with the salt in the Bunsen flame and note the colour given off.
- Repeat the above steps for different salts and note the colour in each case.

Table of results:

Element	Flame colour
Sodium (Na)	Yellow
Potassium (K)	Lilac
Copper (Cu)	Blue-green
Barium (Ba)	Green
Strontium (Sr)	Red
Lithium (Li)	Deep red

Why does the flame test represent evidence for Bohr's theory?

When a metal salt of a particular element is heated the electrons emit light of a certain colour as electrons drop back down from higher to lower levels.

Why does each element produce its own unique atomic spectrum?

Each element produces its own particular colour as each element has a certain number of electrons which are arranged in certain energy levels.

Therefore different electron transitions are available to that element and thus a different line spectrum is produced by each element.

Everyday uses of emission spectra

- Fireworks: salts of strontium and barium are used in firework displays.
- Lasers make use of light released by electronic transitions.

Atomic absorption spectra

Atomic absorption spectrum is the spectrum that is obtained when light is passed through a gaseous sample of an element.

An atomic absorption spectrometer is used to analyse samples of water or blood for heavy metals such as lead or mercury.

The main principle of atomic absorption spectroscopy is that atoms of an element absorb light of a certain frequency which is particular to that element. The amount of light absorbed is directly proportional to the concentration of that element.

During the process, light which is characteristic of the element is passed through an atomised sample of the element in the spectrometer. The amount of light absorbed by the sample is measured by the spectrometer and this information can be used to estimate the concentration of that element present.

Energy levels and sub-levels

Energy level diagram

The diagram below shows first four main energy levels and their sub-levels.

- In a closer and more exact study of the emission line spectra of elements it was noted that what appeared to be a single line on a line spectrum was really two or more lines which were very close together.
- To explain this, scientists proposed that each main level, excluding the first, was made up of a number of sub-levels.
- The sub-levels were assigned the letters s, p, d, f in order of their energy value. The s sub-level was given the lowest energy, and the f sub-level given the highest energy.
- The number of sub-levels is the same as the number of the main level. Therefore main level 1 has one sub-level called the 1s, the second main level 2 has 2 sub-levels – the 2s and 2p sub-levels, and so on.

ENERGY

N = 4

N = 3

N = 2

N = 1

Main energy level

4f
4d
4p
3d
4s

3p
3s

2p
2s

1s

Sublevel

First four main energy levels and their sub-levels

For the Leaving Certificate the electronic configurations of the first 36 elements are required. The order of filling these sub-levels is: 1s, 2s, 2p, 3s, 3p, 4s, 3d, 4p. Note that the 4s sub-level is filled before the 3d as the energy of the 4s is less than that of the 3d.

Modern improvements on Bohr's theory

Bohr's model of the atom where he envisaged electrons as particles revolving around the nucleus was developed and modified by scientists in the 1920s and 1930s.

- In 1923 the French scientist Louis de Broglie proposed that electrons had wave properties and this was shown experimentally to be correct. Electrons were now said to have both a particle and wave nature.
- If an electron has a wave nature then it could not have a definite path about the nucleus as Bohr had proposed.
- Furthermore the German physicist Heisenburg put forward his Uncertainty Principle about the difficulty of locating the position of an electron in an atom.

Heisenburg's uncertainty principle states that it is impossible to measure the position and velocity of an electron at the same time.

Then the Austrian scientist Erwin Schrodinger developed mathematical equations to describe the probability of finding an electron in an atom. As a result of Schrodinger's work, orbitals were used to describe the movement of electrons in an atom.

An atomic orbital is a region of space where it is most likely to find an electron.

The main differences between Bohr's theory and the modern theories are:

- Bohr thought that the electron had particle form only but it has now been shown to have a particle and a wave nature.
- Bohr proposed that the electron had definite orbits about the nucleus. However modern theory uses orbitals to describe the probable location of an electron.

Properties of atomic orbitals

It is required that you know the shapes of the s and p orbitals.

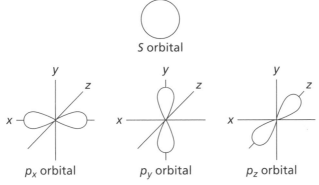

Shapes of s and p orbitals

- Each orbital can hold two electrons. This follows Pauli's exclusion principle where he stated that no more than two electrons can occupy an orbital and when they do they must have opposite spin.

- Aufbau principle: electrons occupy the lowest energy level available when the atom is in the ground state.
- The s orbitals are spherical. There is only one s orbital for each sub-level.
- The p orbitals have a dumb-bell shape. There are three p orbitals for each sub-level. They are called the p_x, the p_y and the p_z orbitals.
- These p orbitals are at right angles to each other as shown in the diagram. It is important to note that any p sub-level can accommodate six electrons.
- There are five d orbitals. It is not required that you know the names or shapes of these orbitals. It is important to note that the d sub-level can accommodate ten electrons.

Sample exam question: 2005 Q4(e) Higher level

What is the difference between a sub-level and an orbital? (6 marks)

Solution

A sub-level is a group of orbitals with the same energy value. For example, the 2p sub-level contains three 2p orbitals (3 marks).

An orbital is a region of space where it is most likely to find an electron (3 marks).

Electronic configurations of atoms

The arrangement of electrons in the various sub-levels is called the electronic configuration. The electronic configuration of the first 36 elements is required for the Leaving Certificate.

Example 1: s, p type configurations

Write out the electronic configurations of carbon, oxygen and nitrogen and explain why nitrogen has extra stability.

Solution

To explain nitrogen's extra stability the arrangement of electrons in the individual orbitals of the 2p sub-level must be examined.

Carbon: $1s^2, 2s^2, 2p_x^1, 2p_y^1$

Nitrogen: $1s^2, 2s^2, 2p_x^1, 2p_y^1, 2p_z^1$

Oxygen: $1s^2, 2s^2, 2p_x^2, 2p_y^1, 2p_z^1$

Note that the individual 2p orbitals are filled singly before filling them in pairs. The above configurations are an example of Hund's rule.

key definition

Hund's rule: When more than one orbital of equal energy exist electrons tend to fill them singly before filling them in pairs.

exam focus

Nitrogen has extra stability as the 2p sub-level is half full and a half-full sub-level is the next most stable to a full sub-level.

Example 2: s, p, d electronic configurations

Write out the electronic configurations of scandium, chromium and copper and explain why copper and chromium have unusual configurations.

Solution

- Scandium has 21 electrons and its electronic configuration is:
  Scandium (Sc): $1s^2, 2s^2, 2p^6, 3s^2, 3p^6, 4s^2, 3d^1$
  Chromium has 24 electrons and its electronic configuration is:
  Chromium (Cr): $1s^2, 2s^2, 2p^6, 3s^2, 3p^6, 4s^1, 3d^5$
  Note the unusual configuration of chromium where one of the 4s electrons moves into the 3d sub-level. Two half-filled sub-levels give extra stability.
- Copper has 29 electrons and its configuration is:
  Cu: $1s^2, 2s^2, 2p^6, 3s^2, 3p^6, 4s^1, 3d^{10}$
  Note the unusual configuration of copper where one of the 4s electrons moves into the 3d sub-level to give extra stability with full 3d and half-filled 4s sub-levels.

Electronic configuration of ions

What is the electronic configuration of the magnesium ion (Mg^{2+})?
What neutral atom has the same configuration?
The magnesium atom has 12 electrons and therefore the magnesium ion has ten electrons as it has lost two electrons (Mg^{2+}). Therefore the electronic configuration of the magnesium ion is:
Mg^{2+}: $1s^2, 2s^2, 2p^6$
This ion has the same configuration as neon.

Atomic radius

key definition

Atomic radius is half the distance between the centres of neighbouring atoms which are joined together by a single covalent bond. For example, the atomic radius in hydrogen is half the distance between the nuclei of the two hydrogen nuclei which are covalently bonded.

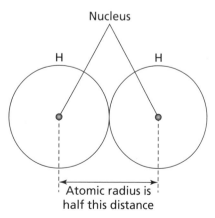

Nucleus

H   H

Atomic radius is half this distance

Atomic radius

Variations in atomic radii

As you go across a period from left to right the atomic radius gradually decreases e.g. from lithium to neon.

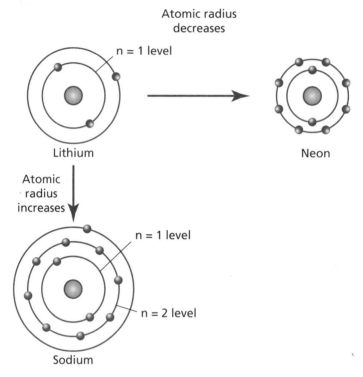

Variations in atomic radius

Why does the atomic radius decrease across a period?

- There is no extra screening of inner electrons as the same main energy level is being filled with electrons.
- The positive nuclear charge (due to protons in the nucleus) is increasing and this causes a greater pull on the electrons drawing them in nearer the nucleus thus reducing the radius.

As you go down a group the atomic radius increases.

- An extra main level is added.
- The pulling effect of the positive nuclear charge is reduced due to the screening effect of the inner electrons.

Ionisation energies

HL

First ionisation energy

First ionisation energy is the energy required to remove the most loosely bound electron from each atom in a mole of gaseous atoms in the ground state.

Example

The first ionisation energy reaction for sodium can be written as

$$Na \rightarrow Na^+ + 1e^-$$

Second ionisation energy

Second ionisation energy is the energy required to remove the second electron from 1 mole of positive ions formed after the first electron had been removed.

Example

$$Na^+ \rightarrow Na^{2+} + 1e^-$$

Note that the second ionisation energy value is always bigger than the first as the second electron is being removed from a positive ion and the positive charge makes it harder to remove the electron as unlike charges attract.

Trends in first ionisation energy values in the periodic table

There is a general increase in first ionisation energy values as you go across a period. This is because:

- the positive nuclear charge is increasing
- the atomic radius is decreasing
- there is no extra screening of the inner electrons as the same energy level is being filled.

All of the above factors make it harder to remove an electron and thus more ionisation energy is needed.

There is a general decrease in first ionisation energies down a group.
This is because:

- the atomic radius is increasing as a main level has been added
- there is the extra screening effect of the inner electrons
- the effect of the positive nuclear charge is reduced.

This leads to a weaker hold on the outer electron making it easier to remove and thus the ionisation energy is smaller.

Exceptions to the general trend

Example

In the period from lithium to neon, beryllium and nitrogen have unusually high first ionisation energy values.

- Beryllium has this high value as it has stable configuration:
  Be: $1s^2, 2s^2$
- Nitrogen has a higher value than oxygen as it too has a more stable configuration:
  N: $1s^2, 2s^2, 2p_x^{\,1}, 2p_y^{\,1}, 2p_z^{\,1}$

This is a stable configuration as the 2p sub-level is half full. Half-full sub-levels are the next most stable to full sub-levels.

Always give the electronic configurations to explain fully the exceptions in ionisation energy trends.

Successive ionisation energies

Let us take the example of removing all the electrons from sodium.
Sodium has the following electronic configuration:
Na: $1s^2, 2s^2, 2p^6, 3s^1$

The following graph drawn shows the ionisation energies for the successive removal of the 11 electrons in sodium.

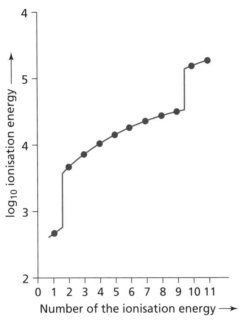

Explanation of graph

The graph demonstrates that ionisation energies do not increase in a regular manner when gradually removing each electron from the sodium atom.

- The second ionisation energy is much greater than the first as the second electron is being removed from a full second main level.
- The next big 'jump' in ionisation energy is on the removal of the tenth electron as this electron is being removed from the full first main level.

These large increases in ionisation energy provide powerful evidence for the existence of energy levels in the atom.

Increase in reactivity down group 1 (Alkali metals)

- As already stated the atomic radius increases as you descend any group.
- In group 1, the alkali metals, the single outermost electron is easier to remove as the pulling power of the positive nucleus is reduced by the screening effect of more inner electrons.
- This, in turn, leads to greater reactivity. Potassium is therefore more reactive than sodium which is in turn more reactive than lithium.

Electronegativity

Electronegativity is the measure the relative attraction atoms in a molecule have for the shared pair of electrons in a covalent bond.

Trends in electronegativity values in the periodic table

Electronegativity values increase across a period.
- There is a decrease in atomic radius.
- The positive nuclear charge is increasing.

Electronegativity values decrease down a group.
- There is an increase in atomic radius as more energy levels are added.
- There is increased screening by inner electrons which reduces the pull on the electrons by the positive nuclear charge.

Sample exam question: 2002 Q5 Higher level

(a) Define first ionisation energy. (8 marks)

(b) Account fully for the trends in ionisation energies of elements across the second period of the periodic table (i.e. Li to Na). (15 marks)

(c) Account for the trend in first ionisation energies of the elements going down group II of the periodic table i.e. the alkaline earth metals. (6 marks)

4 Ionic and Covalent Bonding

aims To revise the following:
- Noble gases and the octet rule
- Ionic bonding
- Covalent bonding
- Polar covalent bond and the test for polarity
- Sigma and pi bonding
- Test for anions

The octet rule

Compounds

A compound is the chemical union of two or more elements. e.g. carbon and oxygen elements react to form carbon dioxide as:

$$C + O_2 \longrightarrow CO_2$$

The noble gases in Group 0 do not tend to react and form compounds. The reason for this is that they have stable configurations e.g. the main level electronic configurations of the first four noble gases are:

Noble gas element	Electronic arrangement
Helium (He)	2
Neon (Ne)	2, 8
Argon (Ar)	2, 8, 8
Krypton (Kr)	2, 8, 18, 8

Most other atoms react to try and achieve the stability of the noble gases. It is important to note that each of the noble gases except helium have eight electrons in their outer level.

key definition

The octet rule states that when bonding occurs most atoms want to have eight electrons in their outer level.

This is a good working rule but there are exceptions e.g. lithium wants to lose one electron to have two electrons in its outer level like helium.

Ionic bonding

An ionic bond is electrostatic force of attraction between oppositely charged ions when electrons are transferred from one atom to another.

An ion is formed when atoms (or groups of atoms) have either lost or gained electrons. A positive ion (cation) has lost one or more electrons e.g. sodium ion (Na^+) has lost one electron. A negative ion (anion) has gained one or more electrons e.g Cl^- has gained one electron.

Example of an ionic bond: Sodium chloride

- Sodium belongs to the alkali metals in Group I. Atoms of elements in this group want to lose one electron to have a stable structure.
- Chlorine belongs to the halogens in Group VII and elements in this group want to gain one electron to have a stable structure.
- Therefore in this bond the sodium atom Na donates its single outer electron to chlorine. The Na atom then becomes the sodium ion (Na^+), the Cl atom then becomes the chloride ion (Cl^-).
- The opposite charges attract each other. This force of attraction holds the ionic bond together as shown in the diagrams below.

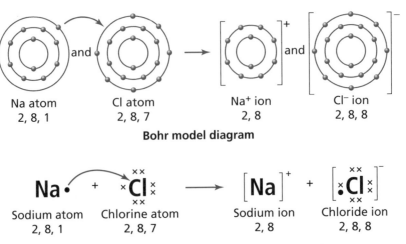

| Na atom | Cl atom | Na^+ ion | Cl^- ion |
| 2, 8, 1 | 2, 8, 7 | 2, 8 | 2, 8, 8 |

Bohr model diagram

| Sodium atom | Chlorine atom | Sodium ion | Chloride ion |
| 2, 8, 1 | 2, 8, 7 | 2, 8 | 2, 8, 8 |

Dot cross diagram showing outer electrons only

The electrostatic force of attraction between sodium and chloride ions is not just one to one but occurs in all directions around an ion. Therefore an ionic compound such as NaCl consists not just of a pair of ions but a network of ions held together in a three-dimensional regular and repeating pattern.

In the case of NaCl this lattice of ions is a cube as shown in the diagram on the right.

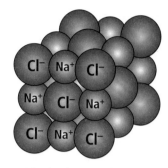

The ionic crystal lattice structure of sodium chloride

Ionic bonding in magnesium fluoride (MgF₂)

- Magnesium belongs to group II (alkaline earth metals). Atoms of elements in this group want to lose two electrons to have a stable structure.
- Fluorine belongs to the halogens and wants to gain one electron to have more stability.
- Therefore magnesium gives one electron each to two fluorine atoms. Magnesium becomes a dipositive ion (Mg^{2+}) and each fluorine atom becomes a single negative ion (F^-).
- The attraction between positive and negative ions holds the bond together.

Magnesium atom 2, 8, 2	Fluorine atom 2, 7	Fluorine atom 2, 7	Magnesium ion 2, 8	Fluoride ion 2, 8	Fluoride ion 2, 8

Dot cross diagram

Covalent bonding

key definition

In this type of bond a pair of electrons is shared between two atoms and each of the bonded atoms contributes one electron to the shared pair.

Pure covalent bonds: Where electrons are shared equally

In the hydrogen gas molecule (H_2), each hydrogen atom contributes one electron to the shared pair. The pair of electrons is shared equally and the two electrons spend most of their time between the two positive nuclei.

The attraction between the positive nuclei and the pair of electrons holds the bond together.

A hydrogen molecule H_2

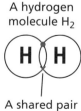

A shared pair of electrons

Covalent bond

The chlorine molecule (Cl_2)

Here two chlorine atoms come together and share two electrons forming a single covalent bond. Each chlorine atom is now stable with an outer level with eight electrons.

Dot cross structure showing covalent bonding in the chlorine molecule

Double covalent bonds: Oxygen molecule (O_2)

Here two oxygen atoms come together and share four electrons forming a double covalent bond. Each oxygen atom is now stable as it has a full outer level with eight electrons.

Dot cross structure showing covalent bonding in the oxygen molecule

Triple covalent bond: Nitrogen gas molecule (N_2)

Here two nitrogen atoms come together and share six electrons forming a triple covalent bond. Each nitrogen atom is now stable with eight electrons in its outer level.

Dot cross structure showing covalent bonding in the nitrogen molecule

Polar covalent bonding

Polar covalent bond: a bond is polar covalent when electrons are shared but not shared equally.

Hydrogen chloride gas molecule (HCl) is an example of polar covalent bond. Here a hydrogen atom shares two electrons with a chlorine atom so that each can then have a full outer level. However chlorine has a higher electronegativity than hydrogen and therefore a greater attraction for electrons. This results in the electron pair being drawn more to the chlorine end of the molecule and the chlorine becoming partially negative $(\delta(-))$ and the hydrogen end being slightly positive $(\delta(+))$.

Polar covalent bonding and the polar charges in hydrogen chloride

Test for polarity in liquids using a charged plastic rod

Procedure

- Set up apparatus as shown in the diagram.
- Open the burette tap and allow the liquid to flow slowly into beaker.
- Bring a charged polythene rod near to the liquid stream.
- If the liquid is polar the liquid stream bends towards the rod. If it is not polar there will be no deflection of stream.

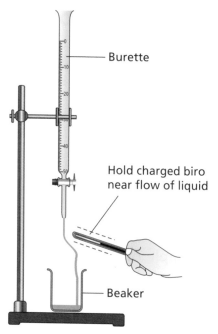

Burette

Hold charged biro near flow of liquid

Beaker

To test for polarity in liquids

Properties of ionic and covalent compounds

The properties of ionic and covalent compounds are compared in the following table.

Ionic compounds e.g. NaCl	Covalent compounds e.g. iodine (I$_2$)
1. Conduct electricity when melted or in solution as their ions are free to move	1. Do not conduct electricity generally
2. Have high melting and boiling points due to the attraction between ions	2. Have low melting and boiling points
3. Most ionic substances dissolve in water	3. Many covalent compounds do not readily dissolve in water
4. Exist as solids at room temperature	4. Exist as liquids and gases usually at room temperature

Ionic substances in everyday life

- Salt (sodium chloride) tablets taken by athletes to replace salt lost by sweating.
- Adding sodium fluoride (NaF) to water supplies to prevent tooth decay.

Polar and non-polar substances in everyday use

- Petrol and methane gas used as fuels are non-polar.
- Water and alcohol are polar.

HL Sigma and pi bonding

Chemical bonding can be described using atomic orbitals instead of the Bohr model. When atomic orbitals overlap they form molecular orbitals. Also when atomic orbitals overlap they form sigma or pi bonds.

Sigma (δ) bond is formed by the head-on overlap of atomic orbitals. Pi (π) bond is formed by the lateral or sideways overlap of atomic orbitals.

Example of sigma bonding: Chlorine gas molecule

The electronic configuration of chlorine is:

Cl: $1s^2\,2s^2 2p^6 3s^2 3p_x^2 3p_y^2 3p_z^1$

Here the $3p_z$ orbitals of the two chlorine atoms overlap to form a sigma covalent bond where two electrons are shared as shown in the diagram.

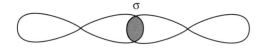

Example of sigma and pi bonding: The nitrogen gas molecule

The electronic configuration of nitrogen is:

N: $1s^2\,2s^2 2p_x^1 2p_y^1 2p_z^1$

When two nitrogen atoms come together the three half-filled 2p orbitals of overlap to form sigma and pi bonds as follows:

- the two $2p_x$ orbitals overlap head on to form a sigma bond
- the two $2p_y$ orbitals overlap in a sideways manner to form a pi bond
- the two $2p_z$ orbitals overlap in a sideways manner to form a pi bond.

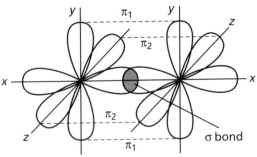

Nitrogen molecule showing sigma and pi bonds

Therefore the nitrogen molecule has one sigma bond and two pi bonds.

A sigma bond is stronger than a pi bond as there is a greater overlap of atomic orbitals in the sigma bond. Also note that:

- a single bond consists of one sigma bond e.g. chlorine
- a double bond consists of one sigma and one pi bond e.g. oxygen
- a triple bond consists of one sigma and two pi bonds e.g. nitrogen.

Electronegativity and prediction of type of bond

Electronegativity is the measure of the relative attraction atoms in a molecule have for the shared pair of electrons in a covalent bond.

The table of electronegativity values can be used to predict whether a bond will be covalent or ionic.

- If electronegativity difference is zero, bond will be 100 per cent non-polar covalent e.g. Hydrogen molecule (H_2).
- If the electronegativity difference is up to and including 1.7, the bond will be polar covalent. A polar covalent bond is where electrons are shared but not shared equally e.g. hydrogen chloride molecule: $H^{\delta(+)} - Cl^{\delta(-)}$ hydrogen chloride molecule.

In this molecule chlorine has an electronegativity value of 3 which is higher than hydrogen (2.1). The electronegativity difference in HCl is 0.9 which is <1.7 and is therefore polar covalent.

- For electronegativity difference greater than 1.7 the bond is assured to be ionic e.g. sodium chloride (NaCl) the electronegativity difference is 2.23 which is >1.7 and is therefore ionic.

Mandatory experiment: Test for anions (Negative ions)

Anion	Test	Observation	Confirmatory test
Carbonate (CO_3^{2-})	Add **dilute HCl** to the solid	Carbon dioxide evolved which turns limewater milky	Add **magnesium sulfate** to solution of solid. A white precipitate of magnesium carbonate is formed Reaction: $MgSO_4 + Na_2CO_3 \rightarrow MgCO_3 + Na_2SO_4$
Hydrogencarbonate (HCO_3^{-})	Add **dilute HCl** to the solid	Carbon dioxide evolved which turns limewater milky	No reaction with magnesium sulfate
Nitrate (NO_3^{-})	Add fresh **FeSO$_4$** solution and concentrated H_2SO_4 to the solid	Brown ring observed	
Chloride (Cl^-)	Add **silver nitrate (AgNO$_3$)** solution. Reaction: $AgNO_3 + NaCl \rightarrow AgCl + NaNO_3$	White precipitate of silver chloride (AgCl) formed	White precipitate is soluble in ammonia

HL

Anion	Test	Observation	Confirmatory test
Sulfite ($SO_3{}^{2-}$)	Add **barium chloride (BaCl₂)** to solid. Reaction: $Ba^{2+} + SO_3{}^{2-} \rightarrow BaSO_3$	White precipitate of barium sulfite formed	Precipitate of barium sulfite is *soluble* in dilute HCl
Sulfate ($SO_4{}^{2-}$)	Add **barium chloride (BaCl₂)** to solid. Reaction: $Ba^{2+} + SO_4{}^{2-} \rightarrow BaSO_4$	White precipitate of barium sulfate formed	Precipitate of barium sulfate *is not soluble* in dilute HCl
Phosphate ($PO_4{}^{3-}$)	**Ammonium molybdate** and **concentrated nitric acid are** added to solid and solution is warmed	Yellow precipitate formed	

Sample exam question: 2004 Q5(a) Higher level

Write the electronic configuration of the nitrogen atom. (5 marks)

Show using dot and cross diagrams, the bond formation in the nitrogen molecule. Describe the bonding in the nitrogen molecule in terms of sigma and pi bonding. (9 marks)

5 Shapes of Covalent Molecules

Note: Chapter 5 is for Higher level students only.

To revise the following:
- Electron pair repulsion theory
- Shapes of molecules
- Symmetry of a molecule and polarity
- Intermolecular forces
- Effect of intermolecular forces on boiling point

Electron pair repulsion theory

In 1940 Sidgwick and Powell proposed a theory to explain the shape of molecules. It was called the Valence Shell Electron Repulsion (VSEPR) Theory where valence shell means outer shell.

The main points of this theory are:
- pairs of electrons will repel each other and take up positions as far apart as possible
- in a covalent molecule there are bond pairs involved in bonding and lone pairs not involved in bonding
- the order of repulsion is:
  lone pair : lone pair > lone pair : bond pair > bond pair : bond pair repulsion
- the shape of a molecule depends on:
  (i) the number of electron pairs around the central atom
  (ii) the type of electron pairs i.e. whether they are lone pairs or bond pairs.

Shapes of molecules

Linear shape for two electron bond pairs – beryllium chloride ($BeCl_2$) molecule

Beryllium chloride and carbon dioxide

In the beryllium chloride ($BeCl_2$) molecule there are two bond pairs of electrons as shown that repel each other to be as far apart as possible. This results in a bond angle of 180°.

Beryllium chloride (BeCl$_2$) is an example of a linear molecule. Carbon dioxide is an example of a linear molecule with two double bonds.

Triangular planar shape for three electron bond pairs – boron trichloride (BCl$_3$)

In the boron trichloride molecule (BCl$_3$) there are three bond pairs of electrons around the central boron atom that repel each other equally. This results in a triangular planar shape which gives the greatest separation between the bond pairs. The bond angle that results is 120°.

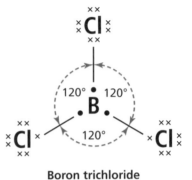

Boron trichloride

This triangular planar shape is typical of Group 13 elements e.g. aluminium(III) chloride (AlCl$_3$) and gallium(III) hydride (GaH$_3$) are also triangular planar.

Tetrahedral shape for four electron pairs – methane (CH$_4$)

In the methane molecule (CH$_4$) there are four bond pairs around the central atom as shown and there is equal repulsion between these pairs resulting in a regular tetrahedron with a tetrahedral bond angle of 109.5°.

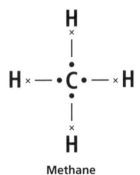

Methane

This tetrahedral shape is typical of group 14 elements – check below carbon in the periodic table! Other examples are silicon hydride (SiH$_4$) or germanium(IV) chloride (GeCl$_4$).

Variation in the tetrahedral bond angle

Ammonia molecule (NH$_3$): Pyramidal shape (Distorted tetrahedral)

In the ammonia molecule there are four pairs of electrons around the central atom but one of these is a lone pair.

As lone pair : lone pair repulsion is greater than bond pair : bond pair repulsion the bond pairs are forced closer together.

This results in the bond angle being reduced to 107°. This produces a pyramidal shape or a distorted tetrahedral shape.

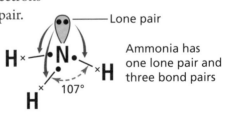

Lone pair

Ammonia has one lone pair and three bond pairs

107°

Ammonia

Other examples can be found using other elements in group 15 e.g. phosphine (PH_3) or arsenic (III) hydride (AsH_3).

Water molecule: V-shape

The water molecule has four pairs of electrons around the central atom.

This time, however, there are two lone pairs and two bond pairs of electrons. Therefore repulsion between lone pairs and bond pairs would be greater than in the case of ammonia. This leads, in turn, to a further reduction in the tetrahedral bond angle to 104°.

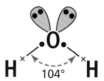

Water has two lone pairs and two bond pairs

The water molecule is said to have a V-shape or a distorted tetrahedral shape.

Other examples of V-shapes are found using group 16 elements e.g. hydrogen sulfide (H_2S) has the same shape as water.

Symmetry of a molecule and polarity

Example 1: Methane (CH_4) where positive and negative centres coincide

A molecule with polar bonds is non-polar overall if the centre of positive charge coincides with the centre of negative charge.

The methane molecule (CH_4) has polar bonds as shown but as the molecule has a regular tetrahedral shape the centre of positive charge and negative charge are in the same place. Therefore the charges cancel each other out and overall the molecule is non-polar.

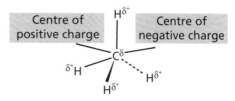

Methane molecule is non-polar overall

Carbon dioxide and boron trifluoride are also non-polar overall even though they have polar bonds for the same reason.

Example 2: Water (H_2O) and ammonia (NH_3) molecules where positive and negative centres are separated

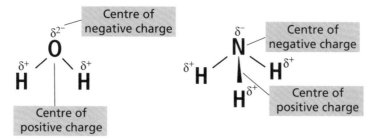

Water and ammonia

A molecule with polar bonds will be polar overall if the centres of positive and negative charges do not coincide.

In the water molecule there are polar bonds as shown and the centres of positive and negative charges are separated. Therefore the charges do not cancel and water is polar overall. This proves that water has a V-shape. If water had a linear shape the charges would cancel and water would be non-polar overall.

Ammonia is also polar as the centre of negative charge is in a different position to the centre of positive charge.

Intramolecular and intermolecular forces

Intramolecular forces are forces within a molecule that hold the atoms of the molecule together e.g. covalent bond.

Intermolecular forces are forces between molecules.

There are three main types of intermolecular forces:

- Van der Waals forces
- Permanent dipole–dipole attractions
- Hydrogen bonding.

Van der Waals forces

Van der Waals forces are forces that arise due to temporary dipoles between molecules.

Let us take the hydrogen molecule as an example. In this molecule two electrons are shared equally between two hydrogen atoms. However at a certain point in time the two shared electrons might be nearer one end of the molecule than the other. This can result in the formation of a temporary dipole in this molecule and in the neighbouring molecule as shown in the diagram.

Van der Waals force

$$H^{\delta(-)}\!-\!H^{\delta(+)} \cdots\cdots H^{\delta(-)}\!-\!H^{\delta(+)}$$

Van der Waals forces between hydrogen molecules

These temporary dipoles are called van der Waals forces and explain why gases such as hydrogen and nitrogen can be liquefied under conditions of high pressure or low temperature when the molecules are closer together. The van der Waals forces are weak forces and are easily separated.

It is important to note that van der Waals forces between molecules with a large number of electrons will be stronger than in the case of a small molecule with a small number of electrons. Therefore oxygen has stronger van der Waals forces than hydrogen.

Permanent dipole–dipole attractions

Permanent dipole–dipole attractions are forces of attraction between the positive pole of one molecule and the negative pole of another molecule.

Example of dipole–dipole attraction, the hydrogen chloride molecule (HCl), is shown in the diagram.

$$\overset{\delta^+}{H}\!-\!\overset{\delta^-}{Cl}\cdots\overset{\delta^+}{H}\!-\!\overset{\delta^-}{Cl}\cdots\overset{\delta^+}{H}\!-\!\overset{\delta^-}{Cl}$$

Dipole–dipole force

Dipole–dipole attraction in hydrogen chloride

In this molecule two electrons are shared unequally in a polar covalent bond. Chlorine has a higher electronegativity than hydrogen and therefore has a greater pull on the electrons.

Therefore the chlorine end of the molecule carries a partially negative charge and the hydrogen end carries a partially positive charge as shown in the diagram.

The attraction between these charges is called dipole–dipole attraction and leads to this molecule having a higher boiling point than a non-polar molecule of similar mass.

Hydrogen bonding

Hydrogen bonding is a particular type of dipole–dipole attraction where hydrogen atoms are bonded to fluorine, oxygen or nitrogen.

Example of hydrogen bonding: Hydrogen fluoride (HF)

- In the hydrogen fluoride molecule fluorine is much more electronegative than hydrogen and has a greater share in the shared pair of electrons.
- Therefore fluorine is partially negative and hydrogen is partially positive. The charges involved here are strong because of the large difference in electronegativity between the two elements.
- This gives rise to a strong attraction between the positive pole in one molecule (on the hydrogen atom) and the negative pole in the other molecule (on the fluorine atom) as shown in the diagram. Other examples of hydrogen bonding are: water (H_2O) and ammonia (NH_3) which are also shown in the diagram.

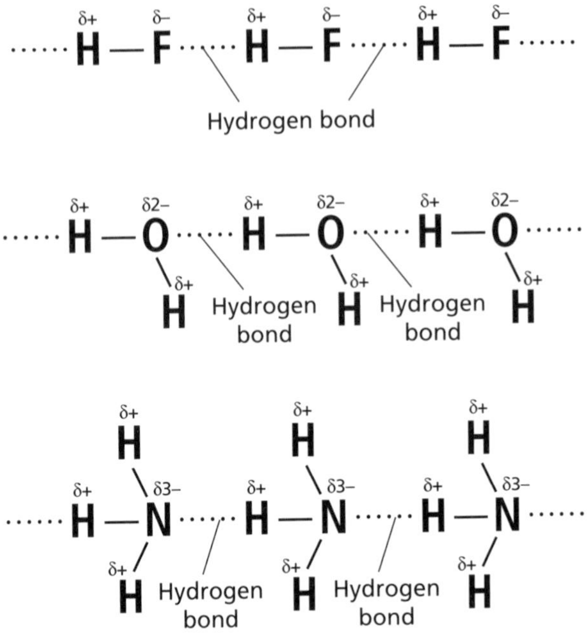

Hydrogen bonding occurs in hydrogen fluoride, water and ammonia.

Hydrogen bonding

Effect of intermolecular forces on boiling points

- Hydrogen bonds are stronger than dipole–dipole attraction which is in turn stronger than van der Waals forces.
- Therefore molecules with hydrogen bonding have much higher boiling points than hydrogen compounds of other elements in the same group. The reason for this is that the molecules are harder to separate and therefore more heat energy is required to separate them.

Comparison of some covalent compounds

- H_2 and O_2

  Oxygen has a higher boiling point than hydrogen as it has stronger van der Waals forces between its molecules than hydrogen.
- H_2O and H_2S (hydrogen sulfide)

Water has a boiling point of 100 °C whereas hydrogen sulfide (H_2S) of only −61°C. The reason for this is that water has strong hydrogen bonding between its molecules but hydrogen sulfide has only weak dipole–dipole attraction.

Sample exam question: 2005 Q4(b) Higher level

What are the possible shapes of molecules of general formula AB_2? (6 marks)

Solution

linear /straight (3 marks)

bent/angular/ 'V' shape (3 marks)

Note that the 6 marks here could be obtained by drawing a correctly shaped diagram using correct examples.

Sample exam question: 2008 Q5(e) (f) Higher level

(e) Explain the term intermolecular force. (6 marks)

(f) Use your knowledge of intermolecular forces to explain why methane has a very low boiling point. The relative molecular mass of methane is only slightly lower than that of water but the boiling point of water is much higher. Suggest a reason for this. (6 marks)

Solution

(e) forces between molecules (6 marks).

(f) very weak intermolecular forces (weak van der Waals, weak dipole–dipole forces) (3 marks).

boiling point of water higher due to strong hydrogen bonds between water molecules (3 marks).

6 Gas Laws and the Mole

To revise the following:
- Diffusion
- Kinetic theory and limitations of the kinetic theory
- Gas laws and an ideal gas
- The mole
- Molar calculations
- Equation of state for an ideal gas
- Mandatory experiment: To find the relative molecular mass of a volatile liquid

Movement of particles in solids, liquids and gases

The particles in solids, liquids and gases show different degrees of movement.
- Solid particles vibrate but maintain a fixed position.
- Liquid particles slide over each other but are still close together.
- Gas particles are far apart and move freely and rapidly.

The freedom of movement depends on how much energy the particles possess. Therefore gas molecules have more energy than solid or liquid particles.

key definition

Diffusion is a process where a substance spreads out through another substance in a uniform manner.

Diffusion demonstrates the movement of particles.

Specified demonstration: Diffusion of ammonia and hydrogen chloride gases

Procedure

- Place two cotton wool plugs, one soaked in hydrochloric acid (HCl) and the other soaked in ammonia (NH_3), in a glass tube as shown.

- A white ring of ammonium chloride is formed nearer the hydrochloric acid end of the tube. The gas molecules of ammonia and hydrogen chloride have diffused from both ends and have reacted to form ammonium chloride.

NH_3 diffuses faster than HCl because of its smaller relative molecular mass.

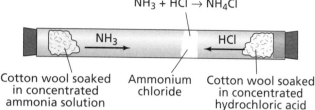

The gases meet here, forming a ring of white powder
$NH_3 + HCl \rightarrow NH_4Cl$

Cotton wool soaked in concentrated ammonia solution

Ammonium chloride

Cotton wool soaked in concentrated hydrochloric acid

The reaction is: $HCl + NH_3 \longrightarrow NH_4Cl$ (ammonium chloride)

- The white ring is formed nearer to the hydrochloric acid end as the molecules of hydrogen chloride have a larger molecular mass and are therefore slower.

Other examples of diffusion are:

- Smoke particles in air e.g. burn some brown paper in air to observe this.
- Diffusion of liquid in liquid can be shown by placing some blue ink at the bottom of a beaker of water. The ink molecules will be seen to spread gradually through the water. Diffusion in liquids is slower than in gases.

Kinetic theory

Main points of the kinetic theory

1. Gas particles are so widely spaced that their own volume is negligible in comparison with the distance between them.
2. Attractive or repulsive forces between gas particles are negligible.
3. The particles move in a constant, rapid, straight-line motion colliding with each other and the walls of the container. This motion is called Brownian motion.
4. Collisions between the molecules of a gas are perfectly elastic i.e. no energy is lost in the collision.
5. Average kinetic energy of the particles is directly proportional to the Kelvin or absolute temperature. Heating the gas increases the movement of the particles and therefore increases the kinetic energy (energy due to movement).

Ideal gas

key definition

An ideal gas obeys all the assumptions of the kinetic theory under all conditions of temperature and pressure.

The limitations of the kinetic theory

- **Limitation 1**: the statement that the volume of gas particles is negligible in comparison with the distance between them is not true in all cases. This would not be true in conditions of high pressure or low temperature as the gas molecules are pushed closer together.
- **Limitation 2**: The statement that gas molecules have no attractive or repulsive forces is not true in situations of high pressure and low temperatures. When the gas particles are closer together van der Waals forces can arise.

Gas laws

1. Boyle's law

In 1662 the Irish scientist Robert Boyle established a relationship between the pressure of a gas and its volume.

Robert Boyle

Boyle's law states that at constant temperature the volume of a fixed mass of gas is inversely proportional to the pressure of the gas.

Boyle's law can be stated mathematically as:
$P \times V = k$ (constant) at constant temperature
where P = pressure, V = volume

2. Charles's law

Charles's law relates the volume of a gas to its temperature.

Charles's law states that at constant pressure the volume of a fixed mass of gas is directly proportional to the absolute temperature (on the Kelvin scale).

Charles's law can be stated mathematically as:
$$V = kT$$
Where V = volume of gas and T = Kelvin temperature

It is important in defining Charles's law to state that the temperature is in Kelvin as this law only applies to temperature on the Kelvin scale.

To convert temperature in degrees Celsius to Kelvin add 273.

Example: 27°C = 273 + 27 = 300 K

3. Combined gas law (General gas law)

This is a combination of Boyle's and Charles's law:

$$\frac{P_1V_1}{T_1} = \frac{P_2V_2}{T_2}$$

This formula is often used to convert a volume at a certain temperature and pressure to a volume at standard temperature and pressure as in the following example.

Sample problem on combined gas law

A sample of nitrogen gas has a volume of 200 cm³ at 27°C and a pressure of 90,000 Pa. Find its volume at standard temperature and pressure (s.t.p.).

Solution

P_1 = Standard pressure = 1×10^5 Pa(N/m²) and P_2 = 90,000 Pa

T_1 = Standard temperature = 273 K   and T_2 = 27 + 273 = 300 K

V_1 = standard volume = ?   and V_2 = 200 cm³

$$\frac{P_1V_1}{T_1} = \frac{P_2V_2}{T_2}$$

$$\frac{1 \times 10^5 \times V_1}{273} = \frac{0.9 \times 10^5 \times 200}{300}$$

$$\Rightarrow V_1 = \text{standard volume} = 163.8 \text{ cm}^3.$$

Gay-Lussac's law of combining volumes

In 1808 the French chemist Joseph Gay-Lussac noticed a pattern in the ratios in which gases react to form products.

key
definition

Gay-Lussac's law states that when gases react, the volumes of the reacting gases and the volumes of any gaseous products are in small whole number ratios to each other, provided the volumes are measured under the same conditions of temperature and pressure.

Avogadro's law

In 1811 the Italian chemist Amedeo Avogadro developed Gay-Lussac's law when he described gases reacting in terms of molecules rather than atoms.

key
definition

Avogadro's law states that equal volumes of gases under the same conditions of temperature and pressure contain equal numbers of molecules.

Amedeo Avogadro

H_2 Cl_2

Equal volumes of gases contain equal numbers of molecules.

As a result of Avogadro's law a mole of a gas could be defined.

The mole

A mole of any gas is that amount of it that contains the Avogadro number of particles i.e. 1 mole $= 6 \times 10^{23}$ particles.

Molar volume

As a consequence of Avogadro's law the molar volume of any gas must be the same under the same conditions of temperature and pressure.

The molar volume at s.t.p. $= 22.4$ litres

Molar calculations dealing in mass

Changing moles to mass in grams

Find the mass of 0.5 moles of calcium hydroxide $(Ca(OH)_2)$.

1 mole of a substance $=$ relative molecular mass expressed in grams

1 mole of $Ca(OH)_2) = 40 + 2 (16 + 1) = 40 + 34 = 74\,g$

0.5 moles $= 74 \times 0.5 = 37\,g$

Changing mass to moles

In changing mass to moles the following formula must be used.

$$\frac{\text{Actual mass}}{\text{Molar mass}} = \text{number of moles}$$

Example

Find the number of moles in 0.64 g of oxygen gas.

$$\frac{\text{Actual mass}}{\text{Molar mass}} = \text{number of moles}$$

$$\frac{0.64}{32} = 0.02 \text{ moles}$$

Changing mass to molecules or atoms

In converting mass to molecules or atoms the following conversion plan is useful.

$$\text{Mass} \xrightarrow[]{\div \text{ molar mass}} \text{Moles} \xrightarrow[]{\times 6 \times 10^{23}} \text{Molecules} \longrightarrow \text{Atoms}$$

Example

Find the number of (i) moles (ii) molecules (iii) atoms in 0.36 g of water.

Conversion plan

$$\text{mass} \longrightarrow \text{moles} \longrightarrow \text{molecules} \longrightarrow \text{atoms}$$

1 mole water = 18 g

$$\frac{0.36}{18} = 0.02 \text{ moles (i)} = 0.02 \times 6 \times 10^{23} \text{ molecules}$$

$$= 1.2 \times 10^{22} \text{ molecules (ii)}$$

As every molecule of water contains three atoms then

$$1.2 \times 10^{22} \text{ molecules} = 3 \times 1.2 \times 10^{22} \text{ atoms}$$

$$= 3.6 \times 10^{22} \text{ atoms. (iii)}$$

Molar volume calculations

In volume calculations it is important to note that:

$$1 \text{ mole} = 22.4 \text{ litres} = 6 \times 10^{23} \text{ molecules.}$$

Changing volume to moles

Find the number of moles in 1.12 litres of oxygen gas.

$$\frac{\text{Volume}}{\text{Molar volume}} = \frac{1.12}{22.4} = 0.05 \text{ moles}$$

Changing from actual volume to moles and then to molecules

$$\frac{\text{Volume}}{\text{Molar volume}} \xrightarrow[]{\times 6 \times 10^{23}} \text{moles} \longrightarrow \text{molecules} \longrightarrow \text{atoms}$$

Sample conversion of volume to molecules

Find the number of (i) moles (ii) molecules (iii) atoms in 112 cm^3 of carbon dioxide gas.

$$\frac{\text{Volume}}{\text{Molar volume}} \longrightarrow \text{moles} \longrightarrow \text{molecules} \longrightarrow \text{atoms}$$

$$\frac{112 \text{ cm}^3}{1000} = 0.112 \text{ litres}$$

1 mole = 22.4 litres

$$\frac{0.112}{22.4} = 0.005 \text{ moles (i)} = 0.005 \times 6 \times 10^{23} \text{ molecules}$$

$$= 3 \times 10^{21} \text{ molecules (ii)}$$

As every molecule of carbon dioxide consists of three atoms then: 3×10^{21} molecules = $3 \times 3 \times 10^{21}$ atoms = 9×10^{21} atoms (iii)

(HL) Converting atoms or molecules to volume

Example

What volume does 3×10^{22} molecules of oxygen occupy?

In this conversion the following pathway can be used.

$$\text{Molecules} \xrightarrow{\div 6 \times 10^{23}} \text{moles} \longrightarrow \text{litres}$$

1 mole of oxygen = 6×10^{23} molecules = 22.4 litres

$$\frac{3 \times 10^{22}}{6 \times 10^{23}} = 0.05 \text{ moles} = 0.05 \times 22.4 \text{ litres}$$

$$= 1.12 \text{ litres}$$

Equation of state for an ideal gas

An ideal gas is a gas that obeys the kinetic theory and the gas laws at all temperatures and pressures. In reality no such gas exists but at ordinary temperatures and pressures most gases would behave like an ideal gas.

Ideal gas equation (equation of state for ideal gas):

$$PV = nRT$$

It is important to use the following standard units in a calculation involving the law.

P = pressure measured in Pascals (Pa) (N/m²)
V = volume in m³ (1 m³ = 1000 litres = 1,000,000 cm³)
T = temperature in Kelvin, N = number of moles.
R = Universal gas constant = 8.3 J K⁻¹mol⁻¹

Typical problem on the ideal gas equation

0.5 g of a gas occupies 200 cm³ at 27°C and at a pressure of 100 kPa. (R = 8.3 J K⁻¹mol⁻¹) Calculate (i) the number of moles of the gas (ii) relative molecular mass of the gas.

Solution

Ideal gas equation:

$$PV = nRT$$

Conversion of units to standard units:

Volume must be converted to m³

The volume given = 200 cm³. To convert to m³ divide by 1,000,000 therefore 200 cm³ = 2×10^{-4} m³

Temperature must be converted to Kelvin

$$27°C + 273 = 300 \text{ K}$$

Pressure must be in Pascals: $100 \text{ kPa} = 100,000 \text{ Pa} = 1 \times 10^5$

$$PV = nRT$$

$$(1 \times 10^5)(2 \times 10^{-4}) = n\,(8.3)\,(300)$$

$$\text{Therefore } n = \frac{(1 \times 10^5)(2 \times 10^{-4})}{8.3 \times 300}$$

(i) number of moles $= n = 0.008$ moles

Therefore 0.008 moles of gas $= 0.5$ g

$$1 \text{ mole} = 62.5$$

(ii) Therefore relative molecular mass of gas $= 62.5$

Sample exam question: 2004 Q10(c) Higher level

State Avogadro's law. (5 marks)

(i) What is an ideal gas? (5 marks)

(ii) State one reason why ammonia gas deviates from ideal behaviour. (3 marks)

(iii) A small quantity of the volatile solvent propanone (C_3H_6O) evaporates at room temperature and pressure. Use the ideal gas equation to calculate the volume, in litres, of propanone vapour formed when 0.29 g of the liquid propanone evaporates at 20 °C and at room pressure of 100 kPa. (12 marks)

Note: (solution to (iii) $= 0.12$ litres)

Mandatory experiment: To find the relative molecular mass of a volatile liquid

A volatile liquid is one with a low boiling point and in this experiment propanone can be used.

Procedure

- Find the mass of a clean dry conical flask together with a circle of aluminium foil and a rubber band. Call this mass m_1.
- Place a small volume of propanone in the flask. Cover the mouth of the flask with the foil and stretch the rubber band around it to make it tight. Make a very small pinhole in the foil.
- Clamp the flask in a beaker of water as shown in the diagram.
- Boil the water in the flask using a hotplate. This causes the propanone to vapourise and drive the air out of the flask. When all the propanone has vapourised the flask

is now full of propanone vapour at 100 °C (373 K).

- The atmospheric pressure can be read on a Bourdon gauge.
- Remove the flask from the beaker and dry the outside of the flask. Allow the flask to cool and reweigh. Call this mass m_2. The mass of the vapour in the flask is $m_2 - m_1$.
- Find the volume of the flask by filling it with water and pouring the water into a graduated cylinder.

  Use the ideal gas equation $PV = nRT$ or the combined gas law

  $$\frac{P_1V_1}{T_1} = \frac{P_2V_2}{T_2}$$ to calculate the relative molecular mass

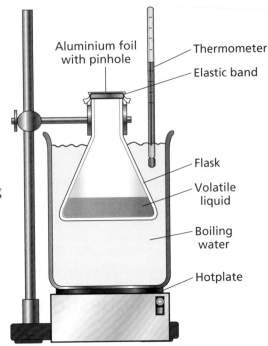

Aluminium foil with pinhole

Thermometer

Elastic band

Flask

Volatile liquid

Boiling water

Hotplate

7 Acid–Base Theories

 To revise the following:
- Acids and bases
- Common acids and bases
- Arrhenius and Bronsted-Lowry theories of acids and bases
- Neutralisation reactions
- Conjugate acids and bases
- Exam question and solution on typical acid-base reaction

Introduction to acids and bases

Everyday acids

Acids are substances that:
- react with metals producing hydrogen gas
- turn blue litmus red.

Hydrochloric acid (HCl), sulfuric acid (H_2SO_4) and nitric acid (HNO_3) are examples of strong acids.

Common everyday acids

- Vinegar containing the weak acid ethanoic acid (CH_3COOH).
- Hydrochloric acid in the stomach to kill bacteria in food.
- Sour milk containing the weak acid lactic acid.

Bases are substances that:

- turn red litmus blue
- react with acids to form salts.

Sodium hydroxide ($NaOH$) and magnesium hydroxide ($Mg(OH)_2$) are examples of strong bases.

Everyday bases

Common everyday bases

- Sodium hydroxide in oven cleaner.
- Sodium carbonate (Na_2CO_3) in washing soda.

Alkalis are bases that dissolve in water e.g. sodium hydroxide. Calcium carbonate, found in limestone, is a base but not an alkali, as it is not soluble in water.

Neutralisation reactions

A neutralisation reaction is a reaction where an acid reacts with a base to form a salt and water.

Example of a neutralisation reaction: hydrochloric acid reacts with sodium hydroxide to form the salt sodium chloride and water as:

$$HCl + NaOH \longrightarrow NaCl + H_2O$$
Sodium chloride

Everyday example of neutralisation

If you have stomach indigestion it is probably due to excess acid (HCl). To neutralise the acid, milk of magnesia can be taken which contains the base magnesium hydroxide $(Mg(OH)_2)$ which neutralises the acid to form the salt magnesium chloride according to the following reaction:

INDIGESTION TABLETS

$$2HCl + Mg(OH)_2 \longrightarrow MgCl_2 + 2H_2O$$

Theories of acids and bases

The Arrhenius theory (1903): The Swedish chemist Arrhenius put forward the following definitions of acids and bases.

An Arrhenius acid is a substance that dissociates in water to produce hydrogen ions (H^+ ions).
e.g. $HCl \longrightarrow H^+ + Cl^-$
hydrochloric acid

Svante Arrhenius

An Arrhenius base is a substance that dissociates in water to produce hydroxide ions (OH^- ions).
e.g. $NaOH \longrightarrow Na^+ + OH^-$
Sodium hydroxide   hydroxide ion

Two major limitations of the Arrhenius theory are:

1. Arrhenius restricted his definitions to aqueous (water) solutions. However other solvents (liquids) like methylbenzene or liquid ammonia could apply.
2. The hydrogen ion does not exist on its own but reacts with water to form the hydronium ion as: $H^+ + H_2O \longrightarrow H_3O^+$

HL Bronsted–Lowry theory

1n 1923 a Danish scientist, Johannes Bronsted, and an English scientist, Thomas Lowry, improved on the Arrhenius theory with more general definitions for acids and bases.

Thomas Lowry

Bronsted–Lowry acid is a proton donor, i.e. it donates H^+ ions

e.g. hydrochloric acid donates a proton

$$HCl \longrightarrow H^+ + Cl^-$$
proton

Bronsted–Lowry base is a proton acceptor

e.g. ammonia is a base and accepts a proton

$$NH_3 + H^+ \longrightarrow NH_4^+ \text{ (ammonium ion)}$$

Other points of the Bronsted–Lowry theory are:

- the stronger the acid the more readily it donates a proton
- the stronger the base the more readily it accepts a proton
- an acid–base reaction involves the transfer of a proton from an acid to a base.

Conjugate acids and bases

- **A conjugate acid is formed when a proton (H^+) is added to a base.**

Example

What is the conjugate acid of water?

$$H^+ \quad + \quad H_2O \quad \longrightarrow \quad H_3O^+$$
$$\qquad\qquad \text{Base} \qquad\quad \text{Conjugate}$$
$$\qquad\qquad\qquad\qquad\qquad \text{acid}$$

- **A conjugate base is formed when a proton (H^+) is removed from an acid.**

Example

What is the conjugate base of sulfuric acid?

$$H_2SO_4 \quad \longrightarrow \quad HSO_4^- \quad + \quad H^+$$
$$\text{Acid} \qquad\quad \text{Conjugate}$$
$$\qquad\qquad\qquad \text{base}$$

- **Conjugate acid/base pair: a pair consisting of an acid and a base that differ by a proton.**

Example

H_2SO_4, HSO_4^- differ by a proton.

It is important to remember that the stronger the acid the weaker the conjugate base that is formed.

Example

Sulfuric acid is a strong acid and has a strong tendency to donate a proton as:

$$H_2SO_4 \quad \longrightarrow \quad HSO_4^- \quad + \quad H^+$$
$$\text{Acid} \qquad\quad \text{Conjugate}$$
$$\qquad\qquad\qquad \text{base}$$

Therefore its conjugate base HSO_4^- has a low tendency to accept a proton and is therefore a weak base.

Sample exam question: 2007 Q7(a) Higher level

Define (i) acid (ii) conjugate pair according to the Bronsted–Lowry theory. (8 marks)
Identify the conjugate acid–base pairs in the following dissociation of nitrous acid (HNO_2):

$$HNO_2 \quad + \quad H_2O \quad \rightleftharpoons \quad NO_2^- \quad + \quad H_3O^+ \text{ (6 marks)}$$

Distinguish between a strong acid and a weak acid. (6 marks)

Solution

(i) An acid is a proton donor. (4 marks)

(ii) Conjugate pairs are any pair consisting of an acid and a base that differ by a proton.

(4 marks)

Identify: HNO_2 + H_2O ⇌ NO_2^- + H_3O^+

acid   base   conjugate base   conjugate acid

Conjugate pairs formed differing by a proton are:

- HNO_2, NO_2^- (3 marks)
- H_2O, H_3O^+ (3 marks)

Strong acid has a strong tendency to donate a proton. (3 marks)

The answer that a strong acid is fully dissociated in water was also acceptable.

Weak acid has a poor tendency to donate a proton. (3 marks)

- The answer that a weak acid is slightly dissociated in water was also acceptable.
- However the answer that a weak acid does not fully dissociate was not acceptable. This again demonstrates the precision required in answering these questions.

8 Acid–Base Titrations

Concentration of solutions

The concentration of a solution is the amount of solute that is dissolved in a given volume of solution.

- A solution is said to be concentrated if there is a large amount of solute in a given volume of solution.
- A solution is said to be dilute if there is a small amount of solute in a given volume of solution.

There are a number of precise ways of expressing concentration.

Concentration in molarity (Moles per litre)

The molarity of a solution is the number of moles of solute per litre of solution.

1 molar solution: when 1 mole of a solute (solid) is dissolved in a solvent (e.g. water) and made up to 1 litre.

Example

1 molar solution of sodium hydroxide is prepared by dissolving 40 g (1 mole) in water and making the solution up to 1 litre.

It is important to note that the chemistry shorthand for 1 mole/litre of NaOH is 1 M NaOH.

Litre mark

1000 cm³
20 °C

1 molar solution = 1 mole in 1 litre
1 molar solution

Converting mass in a certain volume to moles per litre

Example

A solution contains 4.9 g of sulfuric acid in 250 cm³. Find the molarity of this solution.

4.9 g of sulfuric acid in 250 cm³ = 19.6 g in 1000 cm³

1 mole of sulfuric acid = 98 g

$$\frac{19.6}{98} = 0.2 \text{ moles}$$

Therefore molarity of solution = 0.2 moles/litre

Concentration in parts per million (P.P.M.)

key definition

One part per million = one milligram per litre

Example

Convert 0.005 M solution of sodium hydroxide into parts per million (p.p.m.).

1 mole sodium hydroxide = 40 g

First change moles/litre to grams per litre

0.005 moles/litre = (0.005 × 40) g/l = 0.2 g/l

Then multiply by 1000 to change from grams to milligrams

0.2 g/l = 200 mg/l = 200 p.p.m.

Concentration in percentages

Concentration can also be expressed as percentage weight per volume % (w/v) or percentage volume per volume % (v/v) or percentage weight per weight % (w/w). The meanings of these terms are summarised in the following table.

Percentage unit	Example	Meaning
% (w/v) = g/100 cm³	5% (w/v) HCl	5 g HCl in 100 cm³
% (v/v) = cm³/100 cm³	12% (v/v) ethanol	12 cm³ of ethanol in 100 cm³ of solution
% (w/w) = g/100 g	15% (w/w) glucose	15 g of glucose in 100 g of solution

Sample conversion 1

Convert 0.4 M HCl solution into % (w/v).

0.4 moles/litre $= 0.4 \times 36.5$ g/litre

$\qquad = 14.6$ g/1000 cm^3

Now convert to g/100 cm^3 by dividing by 10

$\qquad = 1.46$ g/100 cm$^3 = 1.46\%$ (w/v)

Sample conversion 2

A solution of ethanol is labelled 12% (v/v).

Find the volume of alcohol in 300 cm^3 of this solution.

$\qquad 12\%$ (v/v) $= 12$ cm^3 ethanol in 100 cm^3

$\qquad = 36$ cm^3 of ethanol in 300 cm^3

Primary standard and standard solutions

> A primary standard is a very pure substance which can dissolve easily in water and which can be used to make up a solution of exact concentration.

Anhydrous sodium carbonate is chosen as a primary standard for acid–base titrations as:

- it is available in high purity
- it is stable in air
- it is easily dissolved in water.

Sodium hydroxide cannot be used as a primary standard as:

- it is not available in high purity
- it absorbs water from the air (deliquescent)
- it reacts with carbon dioxide in the air.

Standard solution

> A standard solution is a solution whose exact concentration is known.

Mandatory experiment: To prepare a standard 0.1 M solution of anhydrous sodium carbonate

Procedure

- Weigh 2.65 g of pure anhydrous sodium carbonate solid on a clean dry clock-glass.
- Transfer the solid to a beaker containing about 100 cm^3 deionised water. Using a wash bottle of deionised water wash the clock-glass thoroughly and add the washings to the beaker.

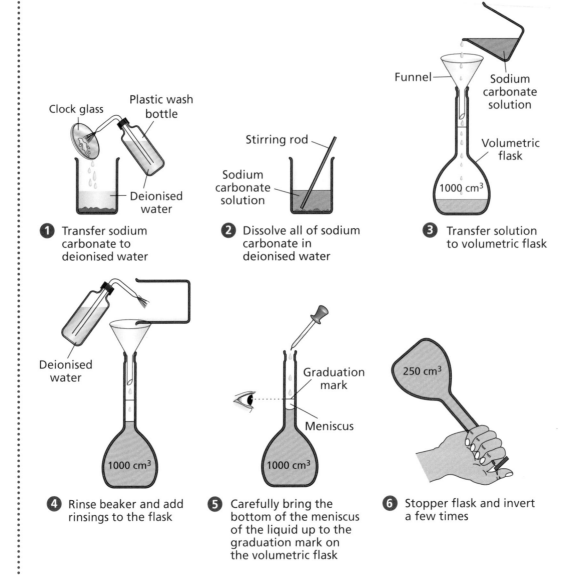

1. Transfer sodium carbonate to deionised water

2. Dissolve all of sodium carbonate in deionised water

3. Transfer solution to volumetric flask

4. Rinse beaker and add rinsings to the flask

5. Carefully bring the bottom of the meniscus of the liquid up to the graduation mark on the volumetric flask

6. Stopper flask and invert a few times

- Stir well to dissolve solid. Heat gently if necessary.
- The cold solution is added to a clean 250 cm^3 volumetric flask which has been rinsed with deionised water. A filter funnel must be used to avoid spills and a stirring rod can be used to direct liquid from the beaker into the funnel.
- The beaker, rod and funnel are washed well and all the washings are added to the flask.
- Fill the flask to within 1 cm^3 of the mark with deionised water and then add dropwise using a dropper until the bottom of the meniscus is on the mark. It is important to read the meniscus at eye level as shown in the diagram.
- Stopper the flask and invert several times for a thorough mix as the long neck of the volumetric flask makes it difficult to get a thorough mix.

General titration procedure

The following section outlines the general procedure used in getting the various items of glassware ready for a titration.

These procedural points appear regularly on the exam and each point generally merits three marks. Therefore if there are nine marks allotted to a question on procedure, three points are necessary.

Setting up burette

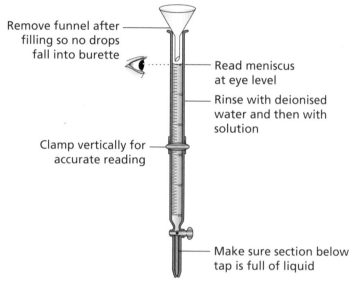

Remove funnel after filling so no drops fall into burette

Read meniscus at eye level

Rinse with deionised water and then with solution

Clamp vertically for accurate reading

Make sure section below tap is full of liquid

Procedure

- Initially wash with deionised water and then with the solution it is to contain. If it was only washed with deionised water the water would dilute the solution.
- Make sure the section below the tap is full of liquid by allowing some of the solution through into a beaker. This is to exclude air bubbles.
- Clamp vertically for accurate reading.
- Read the meniscus at eye level.
- For colourless solutions the bottom of the meniscus is on the zero mark but for dark solutions e.g. potassium manganate(VII) the top of the meniscus is read.

Getting pipette ready

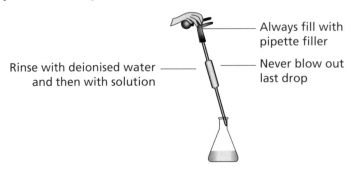

Always fill with
pipette filler

Rinse with deionised water
and then with solution

Never blow out
last drop

- Like the burette, wash with deionised water and then with the solution.
- Always use a pipette filler as many solutions used are of a toxic nature.
- When releasing solution from the pipette into the titration (conical) flask touch the side of the flask with the pipette and allow to run in freely.
- Never blow out the last drop from the pipette as it is graduated to allow for the last drop.

Getting titration flask ready

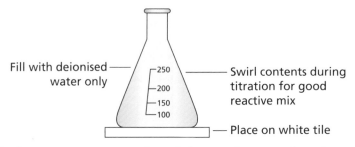

Fill with deionised
water only

250
200
150
100

Swirl contents during
titration for good
reactive mix

Place on white tile

- Unlike the burette or pipette *wash with deionised water only and not with the solution*. Washing with the solution would add to the number of moles delivered to it by the pipette.
- Swirl the flask continuously during the titration to ensure a complete reaction.
- During the titration the sides of the flask can be washed down with deionised water as swirling the flask may cause some of the solution to remain on the sides of the flask. This does not effect the number of moles delivered to it by the pipette.

HL Mandatory experiment: To standardise a solution of hydrochloric acid using a standard solution of sodium carbonate

In this titration the previously prepared standard 0.1 M solution of sodium carbonate is used. It is used to standardise (to find exact concentration of) a given solution of hydrochloric acid.

Procedure

- Rinse the conical flask with deionised water.
- Rinse the pipette with deionised water and then with the standard 0.1 M sodium carbonate solution.
- Transfer 25 cm^3 of sodium carbonate solution into the conical flask using the pipette.
- Using a dropper add three drops of methyl orange indicator. The colour of the solution is now yellow.
- It is important not to use too much indicator. The reason for this is that the indicator is a solution of a weak acid or a weak base and using too much of it would affect the accuracy of the titration.
- Rinse the burette with deionised water and then with the hydrochloric acid solution. Fill the burette above the zero mark and then open the tap and allow the acid to run into a beaker until the bottom of the meniscus is on the mark.
- Add the acid slowly to the sodium carbonate solution in the conical flask. Swirl the conical flask with each addition.
- Note the reading on the burette when the colour changes from yellow to pink. This is a rough end-point.
- Perform at least two more accurate titrations agreeing to within 0.1 cm^3.

Calculating concentrations in volumetric analysis

In calculating unknown concentrations in volumetric analysis the following formula is used:

$$\frac{V_1 M_1}{N_1} = \frac{V_2 M_2}{N_2}$$

Where V = volume of solution, M = molarity of solution and N = number of moles of substance in the balanced equation.

Example

25 cm^3 samples of 0.1 M solution of sodium carbonate were titrated against a hydrochloric acid solution of unknown concentration. The titration figures were 20.4, 20.1, 20.2, 20.3 cm^3. The balanced equation for the reaction is:

$$Na_2CO_3 \ + \ 2HCl \ \longrightarrow \ 2NaCl \ + \ H_2O \ + \ CO_2$$

Find (i) the average titre
    (ii) concentration of HCl in moles/litre and grams/litre

Solution

(i) When calculating the average titre ignore the rough titre of 20.4 cm^3.

$$\text{Average titre} = \frac{20.1 + 20.2 + 20.3}{3} = 20.2$$

(ii) $\dfrac{V_1M_1}{N_1} = \dfrac{V_2M_2}{N_2}$

V_1 = volume of acid = 20.2 cm³, V_2 = volume of base = 25 cm³.

M_1 = molarity of acid = ? M_2 = molarity of base = 0.1

N_1 = number of moles of acid = 2, N_2 = 1

$$\frac{\overset{\text{acid}}{20.2 \times M_1}}{2} = \frac{\overset{\text{base}}{25 \times 0.1}}{1}$$

$$M_1 = 0.25 \text{ moles/litre}$$

1 mole of HCl = 36.5 g

grams/litre = 0.25 × 36.5 = 9.13 g/litre

HL Mandatory experiment: To determine the percentage water of crystallisation in hydrated sodium carbonate ($Na_2CO_3.XH_2O$)

Crystalline sodium carbonate has water molecules in the structure of the crystals and is therefore said to be hydrated. However the water can be removed by evaporation and a powder is formed. This powder form is called anhydrous sodium carbonate. In the following experiment the percentage water in the crystals will be found using a titration with standard HCl.

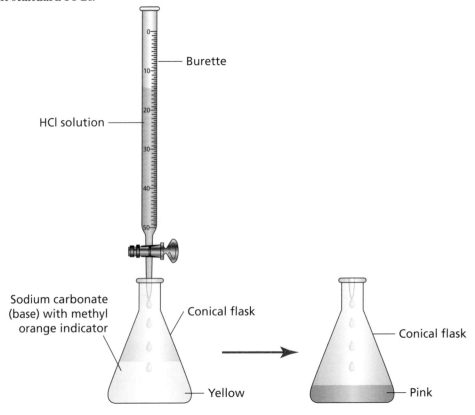

Procedure

- Firstly a solution of the crystalline sodium carbonate is prepared. This is achieved by weighing a certain mass of the crystals on a clock-glass and then transferring them to a beaker of water.
- The solution is then made up to 250 cm³ in a volumetric flask taking the usual precautions.
- Using a pipette place 25 cm³ of the sodium carbonate solution into the conical or titration flask.
- Add three drops of methyl orange indicator. The solution is now yellow.
- Add the standard solution of hydrochloric acid from the burette until the end-point is reached.
- The colour change at the end-point is yellow to pink.

Sample exam question: 2006 Q1 Higher level

The titration reaction is described by the equation:

$$Na_2CO_3 \ + \ 2HCl \ \longrightarrow \ 2NaCl \ + \ H_2O \ + \ CO_2$$

8.2 g of washing soda crystals ($Na_2CO_3 \cdot XH_2O$) were added to water and the solution was made up to 500 cm³. 25 cm³ of this solution required 26.05 cm³ of 0.11 M HCl for complete neutralisation.

Calculate:

(i) the concentration of sodium carbonate in moles/l and grams/l

(ii) the percentage water of crystallisation.

(iii) the value of X, degree of hydration of crystals.

Solution

(i) Calculation of concentration of sodium carbonate in moles/l and grams/l

$$
\begin{array}{cc}
Na_2CO_3 & HCl
\end{array}
$$

$$\frac{V_1M_1}{N_1} = \frac{V_2M_2}{N_2}$$

$$\frac{25 \times M_1}{1} = \frac{26.05 \times 0.11}{2}$$

$$M_1 = 0.0573 \text{ moles/l}$$

$$1 \text{ mole of } Na_2CO_3 = 106 \text{ g}$$

$$= 0.0573 \times 106 \text{ g/l}$$

$$= 6.075 \text{ g/litre}$$

(ii) Calculation of percentage water

$$6.075 \text{ g/litre } Na_2CO_3 = 3.0375 \text{ g/500 cm}^3$$

Therefore 8.2 g of the sodium carbonate crystals contained

$$8.2 - 3.0375 \text{ g of water} = 5.1625 \text{ g of water}$$

$$\text{Percentage water} = \frac{\text{mass of water} \times 100}{\text{mass of crystals}} = \frac{5.1625 \times 100}{8.2} = 62.9\%$$

(iii) To calculate X in the formula

$$X = \frac{\text{moles of water}}{\text{moles of sodium carbonate}} = \frac{5.1625/18}{3.0375/106}$$

$$X = \frac{0.287}{0.0287} = 10$$

Mandatory experiment: To determine the percentage ethanoic acid in vinegar

Ethanoic acid is a weak acid and its concentration is measured using a standard solution of a strong base i.e. sodium hydroxide.

Phenolphthalein indicator is used here as it is suitable for a weak acid/strong base titration changing colour in the pH range 8–11.

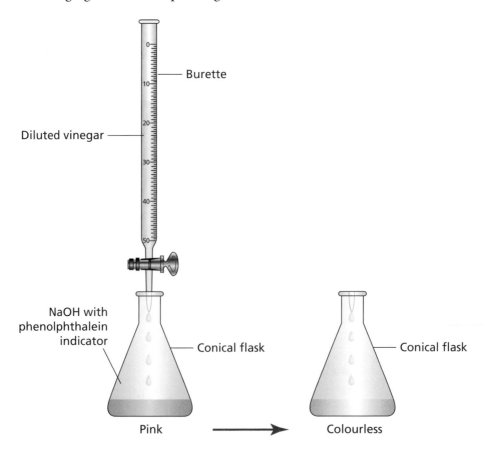

Procedure

- The vinegar must be diluted for this experiment as otherwise too much of the other reagent sodium hydroxide would have to be used.
- The vinegar can be diluted by ten by pipetting 25 cm^3 of the vinegar into a 250 cm^3 volumetric flask and making up to the mark with deionised water.
- Fill the burette to the zero mark with the diluted vinegar solution.
- Using a pipette place 25 cm^3 of 0.1 M NaOH solution into the titration flask. Add three drops of phenolphthalein indicator. The solution now has a pink colour.
- Add the acid slowly from the burette until the colour changes at the end-point from pink to colourless. Repeat until titres agree to within 0.1 cm^3.

Sample calculation: To measure % (w/v) ethanoic acid in vinegar

The equation for the titration reaction is:

$$CH_3COOH \ + \ NaOH \ \longrightarrow \ CH_3COONa \ + \ H_2O$$

A 25 cm^3 sample of vinegar was diluted to 250 cm^3 in a volumetric flask. 22.65 cm^3 of the diluted solution neutralised 25 cm^3 of standard 0.1 M NaOH solution.

Find the concentration of ethanoic acid in the original vinegar solution in (i) moles/litre (ii) g/l and (iii) % (w/v)

Solution

$$CH_3COOH \quad NaOH$$

$$\frac{V_1M_1}{N_1} = \frac{V_2M_2}{N_2}$$

$$\frac{22.65 \times M_1}{1} = \frac{25 \times 0.1}{1}$$

$$M_1 = 0.11 \text{ moles/l diluted vinegar (i)}$$

The vinegar was diluted by 10, therefore original vinegar is 10 times this value: molarity of original vinegar = 1.1 moles/l

Change to grams/litre 1 mole CH_3COOH = 60 g

$$= 1.1 \times 60 \text{ g/l}$$
$$= 66 \text{ g/litre (ii)}$$

To convert to % (w/v) = g/100 cm^3
$$= 6.6 \text{ g/100 cm}^3$$
$$= 6.6\% \text{ (w/v) (iii)}$$

Mandatory experiment: A hydrochloric acid/sodium hydroxide titration and the use of the titration to prepare the salt sodium chloride

(Ordinary level only)

The chemical equation for this titration is

$$HCl \quad + \quad NaOH \quad \longrightarrow \quad NaCl \quad + \quad H_2O$$

Hydrochloric   Sodium   Sodium
acid   hydroxide   chloride

Procedure

(i) To find the end-point accurately.

- Place 25 cm³ of sodium hydroxide in the titration flask using a pipette. Add three drops of methyl orange indicator.
- Fill the burette to the zero mark using the standard solution of hydrochloric acid
- Carry out one rough and two accurate titres.
- Calculate the concentration of the sodium hydroxide in the usual manner.

(ii) To obtain a sample of the salt sodium chloride.

- Place 25 cm³ of sodium hydroxide into a beaker.
- Using the result from part (i) of the experiment add enough of the standard HCl solution to neutralise it.
- Gently heat the solution on a hotplate and evaporate the water. The salt will remain in the beaker.

Redox Titrations

Note: Chapter 9 is for Higher level students only.

 aims To revise the following:
- Potassium manganate and ammonium iron(II) sulfate
- Determination of iron in an iron tablet
- Iodine and sodium thiosulfate titration
- Determination of % w/v of sodium hypochlorite in bleach

Redox titrations involving potassium manganate(VII)

Titrations involving oxidising and reducing reagents are called redox titrations. Potassium manganate(VII) is a strong oxidising agent and it is used in titrations against solutions such as ammonium iron(II) sulfate which are reducing agents. Standard solutions of potassium manganate(VII) are not stable and therefore it is standardised using a standard solution of ammonium iron(II) sulfate which is a very pure stable solution.

Mandatory experiment: Redox titration 1: An ammonium iron(II) sulfate/potassium manganate(VII) titration

The ionic equation for this reaction is:

$$MnO_4^- + 5Fe^{2+} + 8H^+ \longrightarrow Mn^{2+} + 5Fe^{3+} + 4H_2O$$

Procedure
- Fill the burette with a potassium manganate(VII) solution.
- The potassium manganate(VII) has such a dark purple colour that the top of the meniscus is read rather than the bottom.
- In making up the ammonium iron(II) sulfate solution some dilute sulfuric acid is added to ensure that the iron(II) ions (Fe^{2+}) are not oxidised to iron(III) ions (Fe^{3+}).
- Pipette 25 cm³ of the ammonium iron(II) sulfate into a conical flask and add about 20 cm³ of dilute sulfuric acid. Addition of acid before the titration ensures that Mn is reduced from the purple +7 state to the colourless +2 state and not the brown +4 state. In fact, if the solution turns brown during the titration add more acid.

- Note that nitric acid cannot be used as it is an oxidising agent and hydrochloric acid cannot be used as it reacts with potassium manganate(VII).
- Add the potassium manganate(VII) solution slowly from the burette. The manganate solution changes from purple to colourless as it enters the ammonium iron(II) sulfate solution.
- The change from purple to colourless is slow at first but then the change is much faster as the reaction proceeds. The reason for this is that Mn^{2+} ions act as a catalyst for the reaction. This reaction is an important example of autocatalysis where one of the products of a reaction catalyses the reaction.
- The colour change at the end-point is colourless to pink.
- Thus the potassium manganate(VII) acts as its own indicator in this titration.

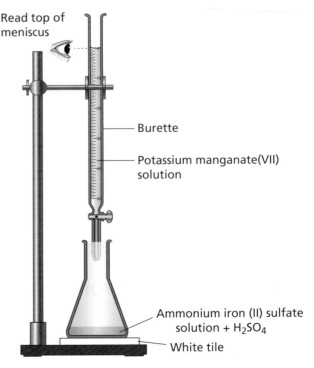

Read top of meniscus

Burette

Potassium manganate(VII) solution

Ammonium iron (II) sulfate solution + H_2SO_4

White tile

Colour change at end-point: colourless to pink

Calculation

$$KMnO_4 \qquad Fe^{2+}$$

titration formula: $\dfrac{V_1 M_1}{1} = \dfrac{V_2 M_2}{5}$

Sample question

A mass of 8.82 g of ammonium iron(II) sulfate crystals $[(NH_4)_2SO_4FeSO_4 \cdot XH_2O]$ was dissolved in deionised water to which some sulfuric acid had been added. The solution was made up accurately to 250 cm³. A burette was filled with 0.02 M solution of potassium manganate(VII) and a number of titrations were carried out.

If 22.5 cm^3 of 0.02 M solution of potassium manganate(VII) was required to fully oxidise 25 cm^3 of the ammonium iron(II) sulfate, calculate the concentration of ammonium iron(II) sulfate solution in:

(i) moles/litre (ii) grams/litre (iii) grams/250 cm^3

Hence find the percentage water of crystallisation and the value of x in the formula.

Solution

$$\underset{\text{Fe}}{\frac{25M_1}{5}} = \underset{KMnO_4}{\frac{(22.5)(0.02)}{1}}$$

$$M_1 = 0.09 \text{ moles/litre (i)}$$
$$= 0.0225 \text{ moles in } 250 \text{ cm}^3$$

1 mole ammonium iron(II) sulfate $= 284$ g

Changing to g/l:
$$0.09 \times 284 = 25.56 \text{ g/litre (ii)}$$

$$\text{in } 250 \text{ cm}^3 \frac{25.56}{4} = 6.39 \text{ g/250 cm}^3 \text{ (iii)}$$

To find the percentage water of crystallisation.

mass of water = mass of crystals − mass of ammonium iron(II) sulfate
$$= 8.82 - 6.39 = 2.43 \text{ g}$$

$$\text{percentage water} = \frac{2.43}{8.82} \times 100 = 27.55\%$$

To find the x in the formula:

$$x = \frac{\text{moles of water}}{\text{moles of ammonium iron(II) sulfate}}$$

$$= \frac{\frac{2.43}{18}}{\frac{6.39}{284}} = \frac{0.135}{0.0025} = 6$$

Mandatory experiment: Redox titration 2: Estimation of iron in an iron tablet

Iron tablets contain iron(II) sulfate ($FeSO_4$) and the following titration is carried out to determine the amount of either iron(II) sulfate or the amount of iron present in each tablet.

Iron tablets are given to people to prevent anaemia (lack of energy). The iron in the tablets is used by the body to make haemoglobin in the red blood cells which carries oxygen around the body.

Procedure

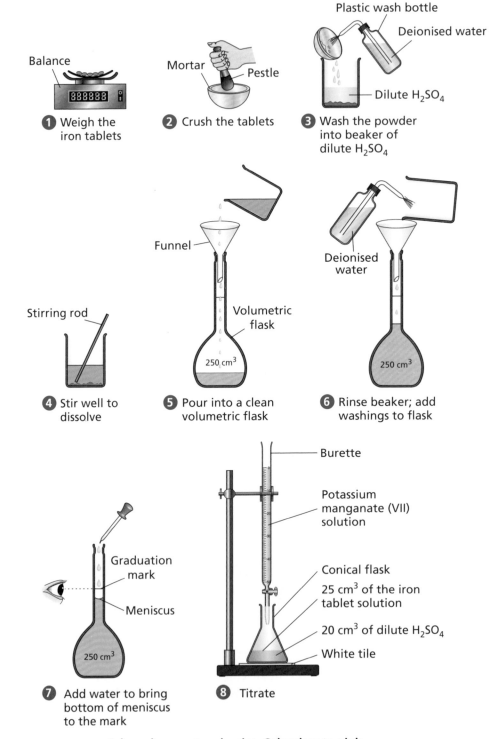

1 Weigh the iron tablets

2 Crush the tablets

Mortar — Pestle

3 Wash the powder into beaker of dilute H_2SO_4

Plastic wash bottle — Deionised water

Dilute H_2SO_4

Balance

4 Stir well to dissolve

Stirring rod

5 Pour into a clean volumetric flask

Funnel — Volumetric flask

$250\ cm^3$

6 Rinse beaker; add washings to flask

Deionised water

$250\ cm^3$

7 Add water to bring bottom of meniscus to the mark

Graduation mark

Meniscus

$250\ cm^3$

8 Titrate

Burette

Potassium manganate (VII) solution

Conical flask

$25\ cm^3$ of the iron tablet solution

$20\ cm^3$ of dilute H_2SO_4

White tile

Colour change at end-point: Colourless to pink

1. Find the mass of five iron tablets using a clean dry clock glass. Five iron tablets are taken as the masses of tablets vary and the average mass of a tablet can be calculated.
2. Grind up the tablets using a mortar and pestle.
3. Transfer the contents of the mortar to a beaker containing 100 cm³ of dilute sulfuric acid. The addition of sulfuric acid at this stage ensures that the iron(II) is not oxidised by oxygen in the air to iron(III). Add all the rinsings of the mortar to the beaker.
4. Stir to fully dissolve the tablet solution. The solution is then transferred to a 250 cm³ volumetric flask using a funnel. Make up to the mark in the usual way. Stopper the flask and invert several times.
5. Fill the burette up to the zero mark with standard potassium manganate(VII) solution. The top of the meniscus is read as potassium manganate(VII) solution has such a dark colour.
6. Pipette 25 cm³ of the iron tablet solution into a conical flask. More sulfuric acid is now added before the titration to ensure that Mn is reduced from the +7 state to the +2 state and not the +4 state.
7. Add the potassium manganate(VII) solution from the burette into the conical flask. There is a colour change from purple to colourless during the titration. If a brown colour should develop add more sulfuric acid to ensure manganese is reduced from purple +7 state to the colourless +2 state and not the brown +4 state.
8. The end-point is reached where there is a colour change from colourless to pink.

Sample calculation of the percentage iron in an iron tablet

Five iron tablets whose total mass is 1.2 g were dissolved in dilute sulfuric acid and the solution was made up to 250 cm³ in a volumetric flask. 25 cm³ of this solution was titrated against 0.02 M potassium manganate(VII) solution and the titre results were: 5.9 cm³, 6.2 cm³, 6.3 cm³, 6.4 cm³.

The equation for the reaction is:

$$MnO_4^- \ + \ 8H^+ \ + \ 5Fe^{2+} \ \longrightarrow \ Mn^{2+} \ + \ 5Fe^{3+} \ + \ 4H_2O$$

Calculate:
 (i) the average titre
 (ii) the concentration of iron(II) in grams/litre
 (iii) the mass of iron(II) present in each tablet
 (iv) the percentage of iron(II) in each tablet.

Solution

(i) average titre $= \dfrac{6.2 + 6.3 + 6.4}{3} = 6.3$

(ii) $KMnO_4$ Fe^{2+}

$$\frac{V_1 M_1}{1} = \frac{V_2 M_2}{5}$$

$$\frac{6.3 \times 0.02}{1} = \frac{25 \times M_2}{5}$$

$M_2 = 0.0252$ moles/litre Fe

$\quad = 0.0252 \times 56$ g/litre

$\quad = 1.411$ g/l

(iii) What is the mass of iron in each tablet?

The solution was made up to 250 cm³

$$= 0.353 \text{ g}/250 \text{ cm}^3 \text{ of Fe}$$

There were five tablets so the mass of Fe in each tablet is:

$$0.353 \div 5 = 0.071 \text{ g}$$

(iv) The percentage of Fe in each tablet $=$

$$\frac{\text{mass of Fe} \times 100}{\text{mass of one tablet}} = \frac{0.071}{0.24} \times 100$$

$$= 29.6\%$$

In redox titrations, ammonium iron(II) sulfate is used as the standard solution. This should not be confused with the standard solution for acid–base titrations which is anhydrous sodium carbonate.

Mandatory experiment: Redox titration 3: Sodium thiosulfate/iodine titration

Sodium thiosulfate acts as a reducing agent towards iodine and therefore can be used to estimate free iodine released during chemical reactions. Sodium thiosulfate reacts with iodine as follows:

$$2S_2O_3^{2-} \quad + \quad I_2 \quad \longrightarrow \quad 2I^- \quad + \quad S_4O_6^{2-}$$

2 moles sodium thiosulfate reacts with 1 mole iodine

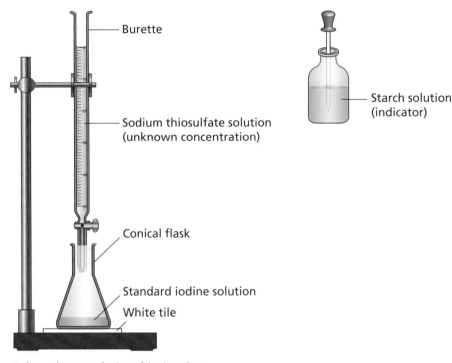

- Burette
- Sodium thiosulfate solution (unknown concentration)
- Starch solution (indicator)
- Conical flask
- Standard iodine solution
- White tile

Colour changes during this titration:

1 Red ⟶ **2** pale yellow Add starch ⟶ **3** blue-black

End-point: blue-black to colourless

Procedure

- The sodium thiosulfate is placed in the burette.
- The iodine solution is placed in the titration flask. As iodine is almost insoluble in water potassium iodide is added to the iodine solution to make it more soluble in water.
- Colour changes during this titration:
  As the sodium thiosulfate is added from the burette:
  1. the reddish-brown colour of the iodine
  2. starts to fade and become straw yellow
  3. at this stage starch indicator is added giving a blue/black colour.
- Continue titrating until the end-point where there is a colour change from blue/black to colourless.

Sample exam question: 2007 Q1 Higher level

20 cm^3 of a sodium thiosulfate solution (Na$_2$S$_2$O$_3$ · 5H$_2$O) required 25 cm^3 of 0.05 M solution of iodine. Find the molarity of the sodium thiosulfate and also find its concentration in grams of crystalline sodium thiosulfate (Na$_2$S$_2$O$_3$ · 5H$_2$O) per litre.

Solution

$$2S_2O_3^{2} \; + \; I_2 \; \longrightarrow \; 2I^- \; + \; S_4O_6^{2-}$$

Sodium thiosulfate Iodine

$$\frac{20 \times M}{2} = \frac{25 \times 0.05}{1}$$
(3 marks)

Molarity = 0.125 moles/litre (3 marks)

To change to grams/litre:

1 mole of Na$_2$S$_2$O$_3$ · 5H$_2$O = 248 g (3 marks)

Therefore   0.125 M = 0.125 × 248 = 31 g/l (3 marks)

(12 marks total)

Mandatory experiment: Redox titration 4: To determine the amount of sodium hypochlorite in bleach

Most household bleaches contain chlorine in the form of sodium hypochlorite (NaOCl). This substance contains the hypochlorite ion (ClO$^-$) also called the chlorate ion. The hypochlorite ion is an oxidising agent and its concentration can be measured by allowing it to oxidise iodide ions to iodine and then measuring the iodine released with standard sodium thiosulfate.

There are two reactions involved in this titration:

Reaction 1: Production of iodine:

$$ClO^- \; + \; 2I^- \; + \; 2H^+ \; \longrightarrow \; Cl^- \; + \; I_2 \; + \; H_2O$$

Reaction 2:

Measurement of concentration of iodine using standard sodium thiosulfate:

$$2Na_2S_2O_3 \; + \; I_2 \; \longrightarrow \; 2NaI \; + \; Na_2S_4O_6$$

Linking the two equations we get:

1 mole NaOCl ≡ 1 mole I$_2$ ≡ 2 moles Na$_2$S$_2$O$_3$

Procedure

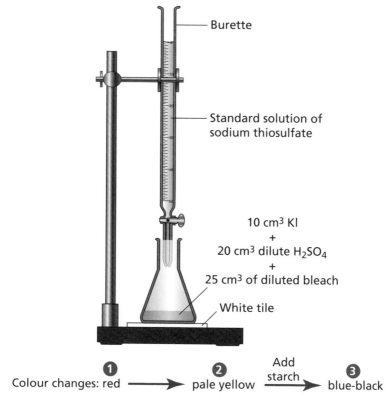

Burette

Standard solution of sodium thiosulfate

10 cm³ KI
+
20 cm³ dilute H₂SO₄
+
25 cm³ of diluted bleach

White tile

① **②** Add starch **③**
Colour changes: red ⟶ pale yellow ⟶ blue-black

End-point: blue-black to colourless

- As domestic bleach is too concentrated it is usually diluted by ten for this experiment as otherwise too much of the other reagents would be needed.
- This dilution is achieved by pipetting 25 cm³ of concentrated bleach into a clean volumetric flask using a funnel. Make up to 250 cm³ in the usual manner.
- Transfer 25 cm³ of the diluted bleach into a conical flask and add 20 cm³ of dilute sulfuric acid and 10 cm³ of potassium iodide solution.
- At this stage reaction 1 above is occurring in the conical flask and the reddish-brown colour of the iodine gas is now visible.
- Place standard sodium thiosulfate solution in the burette and add slowly to the solution in the conical flask.
  Reaction 2 is now occurring in the flask and the iodine is reacting with the thiosulfate. There is a colour change from brown to a light (or straw) yellow.
- At this stage the starch indicator is added and a blue–black colour is obtained (reaction 3).
- Continue titrating until the end-point is reached where there is a colour change from blue-black to colourless.
- Express concentration of sodium hypochlorite in % (w/v) or g/100 cm³.

exam focus

The colour changes for this titration are the same as those for sodium thiosulfate/iodine titration.

Calculation for bleach titration: Sample problem

25 cm^3 of household bleach was diluted to 250 cm^3.

A 25 cm^3 sample of this diluted solution required 32.1 cm^3 of 0.12 M sodium thiosulfate solution.

Find the concentration of sodium hypochlorite in the original bleach in (i) moles/litre (ii) grams/litre (iii) % (w/v).

Solution

From the balanced equation above:

1 mole sodium hypochlorite reacts with 2 moles of sodium thiosulfate

$$\qquad\qquad\quad \text{sodium hypochlorite} \quad \text{sodium thiosulfate}$$

$$\frac{V_1 M_1}{1} = \frac{V_2 M_2}{2}$$

$$25 M_1 = \frac{32.2 \times 0.12}{2}$$

$$M_1 = 0.077 \text{ moles/litre} \quad \text{NaOCl of diluted bleach (i)}$$

As the bleach was diluted by 10:

$$\text{Concentration of original bleach} = 0.077 \times 10 = 0.77 \text{ moles/l}$$

$$1 \text{ mole of NaOCl} = 74.5 \text{ g}$$
$$0.77 \times 74.5 = 57.37 \text{ g/l (ii)}$$
$$= 5.737 \text{ g/100}$$
$$= 5.737 \text{ \% (w/v) (iii)}$$

Everyday examples of bleaches

- Bleaching is a redox reaction. Bleaching can be achieved by oxidation or reduction.
- Sulfur dioxide is an example of a bleach used as a reducing agent. It is used in the paper industry to bleach paper.
- Domestic bleach contains sodium hypochlorite which is an example of a bleach as an oxidising agent. It can be used to make materials whiter or kill bacteria by oxidation.

Note: Chapter 10 is for Higher level students only.

 aims To revise the following:
- To measure the hardness in a water sample
- To find the oxygen content in a sample of water using the Winkler method

Water titration 1

Theory

Hard water is defined as water that does not lather easily with soap but forms a scum instead. It is caused by the presence of calcium (Ca^{2+}) and magnesium ions (Mg^{2+}) in the water.

EDTA solution (ethylenediaminetetraacetic acid) is used to test for hardness because EDTA solution reacts with the calcium and magnesium ions in water and therefore can be used to estimate their concentration. EDTA must be stored in plastic bottles as it reacts with the metal ions in glass.

The disodium salt of EDTA is used in practice as it is purer and more soluble in water.

The disodium salt is represented as Na_2H_2Y and the reaction between it and the calcium ions in the water is usually represented as:

$$H_2Y^{2-} + Ca^{2+} \longrightarrow CaY^{2-} + 2H^+$$

From this reaction it is important to note that:

$$1 \text{ mole of } Ca^{2+} \text{ ions} = 1 \text{ mole EDTA}$$

Mandatory experiment: To measure the total hardness in water using EDTA solution

Procedure

1. The EDTA solution is placed in the burette.
2. Measure out 100 ml of the water to be tested into a clean conical flask using a burette.
3. Add about 2 ml of a buffer solution to the conical flask.
4. A buffer solution is a solution of a weak acid or weak base that resists change in pH. The buffer solution is required in this titration to keep the pH at 10 as otherwise the metal complex formed by the calcium and magnesium ions with the EDTA will break down. This ensures an accurate end-point.

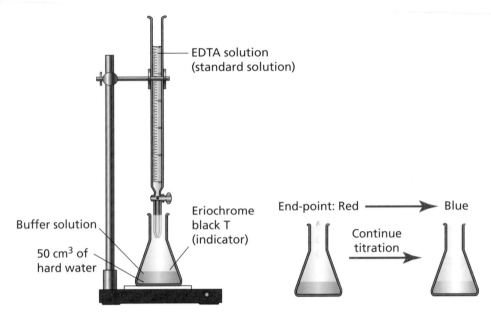

Titration to measure the total hardness in water

5. A pinch of the dry powder indicator Eriochrome Black T is added to the conical flask. The indicator gives a wine-red colour when it combines with the metal ions e.g. calcium ions in the water.

6. When EDTA solution is added from the burette it forms a more stable complex with metal ions and the metal ions break away from the indicator and complex with the EDTA instead.

7. The colour change at the end-point is red to blue when all the metal ions have complexed with the EDTA instead of the indicator. As the end-point approaches add the EDTA solution dropwise, as the reaction between the metal ions and the EDTA is fairly slow.

Sample calculation of hardness in a water sample

100 cm³ of a sample of water required 32.8 cm³ of 0.01 M EDTA for complete reaction with the metal ions present.

(i) Find the total hardness in the water expressed as parts per million (p.p.m.) of calcium carbonate ($CaCO_3$).

(ii) When this water sample was boiled, 100 cm³ of the boiled water only required 15.7 cm³ of 0.01 M EDTA solution. Find the temporary and permanent hardness of the water sample expressed as parts per million (p.p.m.) of calcium carbonate.

$$H_2Y^{2-} + Ca^{2+} \longrightarrow CaY^{2-} + 2H^+$$

From this reaction it is important to note that:
1 mole of Ca^{2+} ions = 1 mole EDTA

(i) Titration formula:
$$\frac{100M_1}{1} = \frac{(32.8)(0.01)}{1}$$
$$\underset{\text{Water}}{} \qquad \underset{\text{EDTA}}{}$$
$$M_1 = 0.00328 \text{ moles/litre } CaCO_3$$

Change to grams/litre: 1 mole $CaCO_3$ = 100 g

$$0.00328 \times 100 = 0.328 \text{ g/litre}$$

1 part per million = 1 mg/litre

Change to mg/l: $0.328 \times 1000 = 328$ mg/l

$$\text{total hardness} = 328 \text{ p.p.m.}$$

(ii) When the water is boiled temporary hardness is removed:

Titration

formula: $\dfrac{100M_1}{1} = \dfrac{(15.7)(0.01)}{1}$

$\quad\quad$ Water $\quad\quad$ EDTA

$$M_1 = 0.00157 \text{ moles/litre } CaCO_3$$

Change to grams/litre: $0.00157 \times 100 = 0.157$ g/litre

Change to mg/l: $0.157 \times 1000 = 157$ mg/l

$$\text{permanent hardness} = 157 \text{ p.p.m.}$$

Temporary hardness = total hardness − permanent

$$= 328 - 157 = 171 \text{ p.p.m.}$$

Mandatory experiment: Water titration 2: Winkler method to determine the dissolved oxygen content in a sample of water

Procedure

- Rinse a stoppered bottle of about 250 ml capacity initially with deionised water and then with the water to be analysed ensuring that the sides of the bottle are thoroughly wet. This ensures that there are no trapped air bubbles as this would add to the oxygen content.
- Fill the bottle with water and replace the stopper immediately as some oxygen may be absorbed from the air. It is important to carry out the Winkler method immediately after sample is collected as the oxygen content changes with time.
- Using a long pipette add 1 cm³ of Winkler's reagent to the bottom of the bottle. Winkler's reagent is a mixture of potassium iodide (KI) and sodium hydroxide (NaOH). Also using a long pipette add 1 cm³ of Manganese(II) sulfate to the bottom of the bottle. Both of these solutions added are concentrated so that very little of the water under test needs to be replaced and therefore the change in oxygen content is minimised. The solutions are added well below surface to ensure they are not displaced when the stopper is replaced.
- A white precipitate of manganese hydroxide is now formed due to the reaction between manganese ions from the manganese sulfate and the hydroxide ions from the KOH. The reaction is:

$$Mn^{2+} + 2OH^- \longrightarrow Mn(OH)_2$$
$$\text{White ppt. of manganese hydroxide}$$

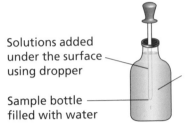

Solutions added under the surface using dropper

Sample bottle filled with water

Solutions added and their effect:

Add (i) $MnSO_4$
    (ii) Winkler's reagent (KI + NaOH):
      a white precipitate forms which turns brown
    (iii) Conc. H_2SO_4:
      brown ppt disappears and a red-brown
      colour of I_2 appears

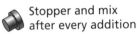

Stopper and mix after every addition

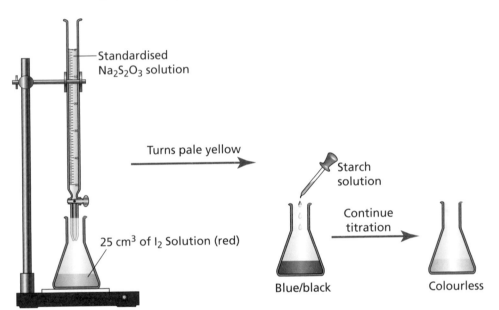

Standardised $Na_2S_2O_3$ solution

Turns pale yellow

Starch solution

25 cm³ of I_2 Solution (red)

Continue titration

Blue/black

Colourless

Winkler method to measure the dissolved oxygen in a water sample

- The manganese hydroxide reacts with the oxygen in the water to form a brown precipitate of manganese(III) oxide.

$$4Mn(OH)_2 \quad + \ O_2 \longrightarrow \quad 2Mn_2O_3 \quad + \ 4H_2O$$
Manganese hydroxide $\qquad\qquad$ Manganese(III) oxide

It is important to note that if the water is badly polluted there will not be a colour change from white to brown as there is no oxygen in the water.

- About 2 cm³ of concentrated sulfuric acid is now carefully added to the bottle. Stopper the bottle and invert to mix thoroughly. Iodine is now produced and the colour of the solution is a reddish brown.

$$Mn_2O_3 + 2I^- + 6H^+ \longrightarrow 2Mn^{2+} + I_2 + 3H_2O$$

- The concentration of the liberated iodine released in this experiment can be estimated by titration with sodium thiosulfate using starch indicator. The reaction is:

$$I_2 + 2Na_2S_2O_3 \longrightarrow 2NaI + Na_2S_4O_6$$

This titration has already been described in redox titrations.

The starch indicator is added when the solution goes pale yellow and the colour change at the end-point is blue-black to colourless.

The concentration of the iodine can then be used to estimate the concentration of dissolved oxygen in the water.

Sample calculation on measuring dissolved oxygen

A 100 cm^3 sample of water was analysed for dissolved oxygen by the Winkler method. The iodine released required 4.8 cm^3 of 0.02 M sodium thiosulfate solution. Calculate the concentration of dissolved oxygen in the water in parts per million.

Solution

From the above reactions the following ratios apply:

$$1 \text{ mole } O_2 = 2 \text{ moles } Mn_2O_3 = 2 \text{ moles } I_2 = 4 \text{ moles } Na_2S_2O_3$$

Therefore the titration formula is:

Oxygen   sodium thiosulfate

$$\frac{V_1M_1}{1} = \frac{V_2M_2}{4}$$

$$\frac{100 \, M_1}{1} = \frac{4.8 \times 0.02}{4}$$

$M_1 = 0.00024$ mol/l

     $= 0.00024 \times 32$ g/l

     $= 0.00768$ g/l of oxygen

     $= 0.00768 \times 1000$ mg/l of oxygen

     $= 7.68$ mg/l $= 7.68$ p.p.m. of oxygen

Sample exam question: 2004 Q1(d) Higher level

In the experiment it was found that 100 cm^3 of the water required an average titre of 8.1 cm^3 of 0.01 M EDTA solution. Calculate the total hardness in (i) moles/litre (ii) grams of $CaCO_3$ per litre and (iii) p.p.m. expressed in terms of $CaCO_3$.

To revise the following:

- Hard water
- Water treatment for domestic use
- Sewage treatment
- Analysis of water

Hard water

key definition

Hard water is water that does not easily form a lather with soap.

Hardness in water is caused by the presence of calcium ions (Ca^{2+}) and magnesium ions (Mg^{2+}). These ions react with the water to form a scum instead of a lather.

There are two types of hardness:

1. temporary hardness, which can be removed by boiling
2. permanent hardness, which cannot be removed by boiling.

Temporary hardness

Causes of temporary hardness

- Calcium hydrogencarbonate $(Ca(HCO_3)_2)$
- Magnesium hydrogencarbonate $(Mg(HCO_3)_2)$.

Temporary hardness is found in a limestone area where the carbonic acid in rain water dissolves the limestone as in the following reaction.

$$CaCO_3 \quad + \quad H_2CO_3 \quad \longrightarrow \quad Ca(HCO_3)_2$$

Calcium carbonate　　　Carbonic acid　　　　　　Calcium hydrogencarbonate

Cure for temporary hardness: boiling the water as this reverses the above reaction and breaks down the soluble calcium hydrogencarbonate into the insoluble calcium carbonate.

$$Ca(HCO_3)_2 \quad \longrightarrow \quad CaCO_3 \quad + \quad H_2CO_3$$

Calcium hydrogencarbonate　　　　Calcium carbonate

It is important to know the chemical equations for the cause and cure of temporary hardness. Note that one reaction is the reverse of the other.

The calcium carbonate formed in this reaction is often called 'limescale' or 'fur' and can cause blockage of heating pipes.

Testing for scale deposits

If scale deposit is scraped off the bottom of a kettle, the calcium carbonate in the deposit can be used to produce carbon dioxide when reacted with dilute hydrochloric acid as in this reaction.

$$CaCO_3 \quad + \quad 2HCl \quad \longrightarrow \quad CaCl_2 \quad + H_2O + CO_2$$

Calcium carbonate   Hydrochloric acid   Calcium chloride

Permanent hardness

Causes of permanent hardness

- Calcium chloride ($CaCl_2$) and calcium sulfate ($CaSO_4$)
- Magnesium chloride ($MgCl_2$) and magnesium sulfate ($MgSO_4$).

Permanent hardness is removed by ion exchange where the calcium and magnesium ions in the water are swapped with other ions e.g. sodium ions that don't cause hardness.

To remove permanent hardness by ion exchange

The easiest way to remove permanent hardness from water is to pass the water through an ion-exchange resin as in the diagram.

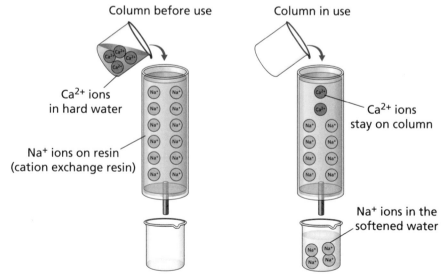

Removing hardness using an ion-exchange resin

Most common ion-exchange resins contain sodium ions (Na^+) and can be represented as Na_2R. As the water passes through the ion-exchange column the sodium ions are exchanged with calcium or magnesium ions as in the following representative reaction.

$$Na_2R + Ca^{2+} \longrightarrow 2Na^+ + CaR$$
resin

As the sodium ions do not cause hardness, the water that emerges from the ion-exchanger is soft.

Permanent hardness can also be removed by distillation of the water but this is an expensive method.

Using ion-exchange resin to make deionised water

In making deionised water there are two different resins used. One resin removes the positive ions and replaces them with hydrogen ions (H^+); the other resin removes the negative ions and replaces them with hydroxyl ions (OH^-). The hydrogen ions and hydroxyl ions recombine to form water.

$$H^+ + OH^- \longrightarrow H_2O$$

The advantages and disadvantages of hard water are given in the table below.

Advantages	Disadvantages
Contains calcium for bones and teeth	Blocks heating pipes
Nice taste	Wastes soap
Good for brewing	Produces scum

What is the difference between deionised water and distilled water?

Distilled water is purer than deionised water as deionised water has only the ions removed but distilled water has ions as well as covalent substances (e.g. chlorine) removed.

Water treatment for domestic use

To make water suitable for human consumption it is put through a number of stages which are described below.

1. **Screening:** the water from the lake or river is passed through metal grids where floating matter like loose leaves or twigs is removed.
2. **Flocculation:** suspended solids in water e.g. clay particles are caused to gather together in clumps by flocculating agents such as aluminium sulfate.
3. **Settling or sedimentation:** the water is passed into settling tanks where most of the suspended matter settles out of the water due to flocculation.

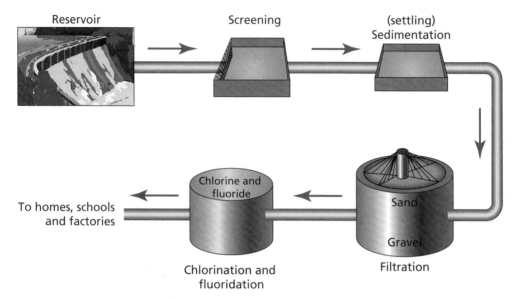

Water treatment for domestic use

4. **Filtration:** the remaining suspended particles in water are removed by passing water through sand filter beds. These filter beds have fine sand on top and coarse sand and gravel below.
5. **Chlorination:** chlorine or chlorine compounds are added to the water to kill any disease-causing microorganisms.
6. **Fluoridation:** fluoride compounds such as sodium fluoride are added to the water to prevent tooth decay.
7. **pH adjustment:** the treated water should be slightly basic. If the water was acidic corrosion of pipes could occur. Calcium hydroxide or lime is added if the water is too acidic. If the water is too basic sulfuric acid is added.

Water analysis

Mandatory experiment: To determine (i) the total suspended solids (ii) total dissolved solids in water (iii) pH in a water sample

(i) Total suspended solids
Procedure
1. Find the mass of a dry filter paper.
2. Place the filter paper in a filter funnel and filter one litre of a water sample.
3. Dry the filter paper by placing it in an oven set at 100 °C. Re-weigh the filter paper.
4. By subtraction find the mass of suspended solids.
5. Find the mass of suspended solids expressing them as p.p.m. or mg/litre

(ii) Total dissolved solids

Procedure

1. Find the mass of a clean dry beaker.
2. Pour 100 cm³ of the filtered water from the previous experiment into the beaker.
3. Evaporate the water in the beaker in an oven set at 100 °C.
4. Reweigh the beaker when it is cool.
5. Find the increase in mass of the beaker – this is the total dissolved solids in the water. Express this mass as mg/litre or p.p.m.

(iii) To measure pH of the water sample

The most accurate way of measuring pH is using a pH meter which gives a direct reading of pH.

Sample problem on measuring suspended solids in water

250 cm³ of a sample of water was filtered and the mass of the filter paper increased by 0.35 g. Find the mass of suspended solids in the water expressed as parts per million.

Solution

$$\text{total suspended solids} = 0.35 \text{ g in } 250 \text{ cm}^3$$
$$= 1.4 \text{ g in } 1000 \text{ cm}^3$$
$$= 1400 \text{ mg/litre}$$
$$= 1400 \text{ p.p.m.}$$

Mandatory experiment: To estimate the concentration of free chlorine in a sample of swimming pool water

Chlorine is added to swimming pool water in the form of calcium hypochlorite $Ca(OCl)_2$. It forms hypochlorous acid in the water which kills harmful bacteria by oxidising them. Hypochlorous acid dissociates in water to form the hypochlorite ion as follows:

$$HOCl \rightleftharpoons H^+ + OCl^-$$

key definition

Free chlorine in water is chlorine which is present as hypochlorous acid or the hypochlorite ion.

Hypochlorous acid has a greater ability to kill bacteria than the hypochlorite ion so the pH of the water is adjusted to keep reaction going to the left (by Le Chatelier's principle).

The comparator method to estimate the free chlorine in swimming pool water

The main principle of this method is that the intensity of the pink colour produced on adding DPD to the water is a measure of the concentration of the free chlorine present.

Procedure

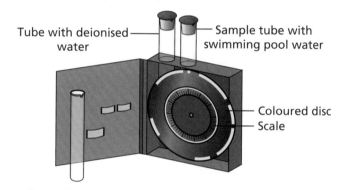

Tube with deionised water — Sample tube with swimming pool water

Coloured disc
Scale

Hach test kit to measure the free chlorine in a water sample

- Place 5 cm^3 of deionised water in one of the viewing tubes. This tube is used for comparison and is placed in the top left hand opening of the comparator box.
- Place 5 cm^3 of swimming pool water in the other viewing tube. Add a DPD tablet to this tube. Note the pink colour of the solution. Place this tube in the comparator box beside the other viewing tube.
- Rotate the coloured disc in the comparator until a matching colour is found for the swimming pool sample.
- Read off the value for free chlorine in p.p.m. Swimming pool water must be kept in the range 1–5 p.p.m. of free chlorine for the safety of the swimmers.

Pollution of water and sewage treatment

Pollution in water can occur when materials such as sewage or silage effluent are discharged into the water. Materials like sewage and silage lead to eutrophication and deoxygenation of the water.

Eutrophication is the enrichment of water by nutrients which leads to excessive growth of algae in the water.

These algae are short-lived and when they decay they are broken down by bacteria, which leads to deoxygenation of the water. This lack of oxygen in the water can lead to fish kills for example.

The biochemical oxygen demand or B.O.D. test was introduced to measure the demand made on oxygen in the water by bacteria and other microorganisms.

B.O.D. is defined as the amount of dissolved oxygen consumed by biochemical action when a sample of water is kept in the dark at 20 °C for five days.

The water is kept in the dark to prevent photosynthesis by small plants in the water which would release oxygen back into the water. Five days is chosen because most organic matter is broken down in that time.

For the B.O.D. test the water under investigation is usually diluted with well oxygenated water beforehand. This ensures that there is sufficient oxygen present in the water for the microorganisms present and enables a second reading of oxygen content to be taken after five days.

Sample exam question: Calculation of oxygen content in B.O.D. test: 1992 Higher level

A sample of waste water was diluted from 25 cm³ to 1 litre with well oxygenated pure water. The water was analysed immediately and its oxygen concentration was found to be 12.8 p.p.m. After five days in the dark at 20 °C the oxygen concentration was measured at 8.2 p.p.m. Calculate the B.O.D. of the polluted water.

Solution

To get the B.O.D. of the diluted water subtract the two values

$$12.8 - 8.2 = 4.6 \text{ p.p.m.}$$

The water was diluted from 25 cm³ to 1000 cm³ i.e. 40 times

Therefore B.O.D. of the polluted water is 40 times the diluted value = $4.6 \times 40 =$ 184 p.p.m.

Sewage treatment

There are three main stages in sewage treatment:

Stage 1: Primary treatment (Physical)

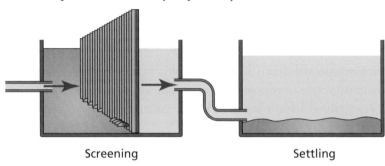

Screening   Settling

Primary sewage treatment

The primary treatment of sewage is a physical process where the sewage is passed through metal screens. The large objects are removed and the liquid is transferred to settling tanks where more solid material is allowed to settle out of the water.

Stage 2: Secondary treatment (Biological oxidation)

The liquid is now fed into aerated tanks where the organic material in the sewage is broken down by bacteria into simpler compounds such as nitrates and phosphates. The tanks are kept aerated by mechanical agitators or air pumps so that the aerobic bacteria have a constant supply of oxygen.

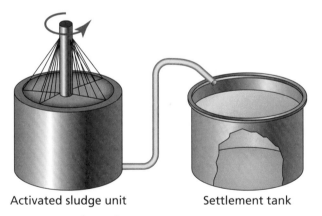

Activated sludge unit   Settlement tank

Secondary sewage treatment

Stage 3: Tertiary treatment (Chemical)

The nitrates and phosphates formed in stage 2 could cause eutrophication if allowed to pass into the waterways.

To remove the phosphates aluminium sulfate is added to the water. To remove the nitrates bacteria are added to the water and they convert the nitrates to nitrogen gas.

(HL) Heavy metal pollution of water

Heavy metal consists of metals such as lead (Pb), mercury (Hg) and cadmium (Cd), which have high atomic masses. These metals are poisonous and must be removed from the water. They get into water when used batteries are dumped or as industrial waste from industries such as mining.

Detection of heavy metals in water

Atomic absorption spectrometers are used to detect the presence of heavy metals in water. The main principle of this method is that atoms of the metal absorb light of a particular wavelength which is particular to the metal. The amount of light absorbed is a measure of the concentration of the metal.

Removal of heavy metals in the water

Heavy metal ions are removed from water by reaction with dilute HCl which causes them to precipitate out of the water as represented by the following reaction:

$$2HCl + Pb^{2+} \longrightarrow PbCl_2 + 2H^+$$

Sample exam question: 2002 Q9(b) Higher level

(i) **Distinguish between the primary and secondary stages of sewage treatment. (12 marks)**

(ii) **What is the purpose of tertiary treatment? (6 marks)**

Solution

(i) Removal of solids (large particles)/physical   (3 marks)
   By screening (metal screens)/physical   (3 marks)
   Secondary: oxidation/breakdown/use of oxygen   (3 marks)
   By microorganisms(bacteria)/biological   (3 marks)

(ii) Tertiary: removal of nitrates (nitrogen compounds)   (3 marks)
   and Phosphates (phosphorus compounds)   (3 marks)

aims To revise the following:
- pH scale and measurement of pH
- pH calculations for strong acids and bases
- pH calculations for weak acids and bases
- Theory of acid-base indicators
- Titration curves and choice of indicator

pH of strong acids and bases

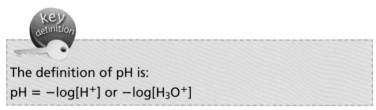

key definition

The definition of pH is:
$$pH = -\log[H^+] \text{ or } -\log[H_3O^+]$$

The square brackets in the formula above mean that concentration of H^+ must be in moles/litre.

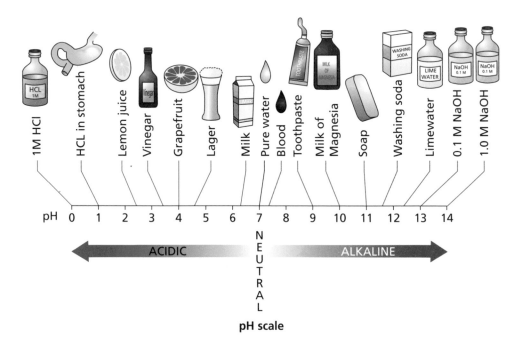

1M HCl — HCL in stomach — Lemon juice — Vinegar — Grapefruit — Lager — Milk — Pure water — Blood — Toothpaste — Milk of Magnesia — Soap — Washing soda — Limewater — 0.1 M NaOH — 1.0 M NaOH

pH 0 1 2 3 4 5 6 7 8 9 10 11 12 13 14

ACIDIC   NEUTRAL   ALKALINE

pH scale

Features of pH scale

- The pH scale measures the acidity or basicity of a solution.
- The scale extends from 0 to 14.
- Solutions with a pH of less than 7 are acidic e.g. HCl.
- Solutions with a pH greater than 7 are basic e.g. NaOH.
- Pure water is neutral with a pH of 7.

What are the limitations of the pH scale?

- Only suitable for dilute aqueous solutions (does not work in concentrated solutions).
- Only gives values between 0 and 14.

Measurement of pH

pH values are measured accurately using a pH meter which gives a direct reading of the pH.

pH calculations for strong acids

key definition

A strong acid or base fully dissociates in aqueous solution.

Sample problem: Find the pH of 0.2 M HCl

Always write the dissociation reaction first.

Hydrochloric acid is a strong acid and fully dissociates as follows:

$$HCl \longrightarrow H^+ + Cl^-$$
$$0.2 \text{ moles} \qquad\qquad 0.2 \text{ moles}$$

Note that HCl is said to be monoprotic or monobasic as it only produces one proton on dissociation.

Therefore $[H^+] = 0.2$ moles/litre

$$pH = -\log[H^+] = -\log[0.2] = 0.6990$$

Sample problem: Find the pH of 0.2 M H₂SO₄

Sulfuric acid (H_2SO_4) is said to be diprotic or dibasic as, on dissociation, it produces two hydrogen ions in the reaction.

$$H_2SO_4 \longrightarrow 2H^+ + SO_4^{2-}$$

Therefore on dissociation: 0.2 moles of H_2SO_4 produces 0.4 moles of H^+ ions

$$pH = -\log[H^+] = -\log[0.4] = 0.3979$$

Sample problem: Find pH of a solution of 4.9 g H₂SO₄ in 200 cm³ of solution

In this type of problem the molarity or moles/litre of the solution must be found first.

4.9 g H_2SO_4 in 200 cm³ = 24.5 g H_2SO_4 in 1000 cm³

Now convert 24.5 g to moles:

$$\frac{\text{actual mass}}{\text{molar mass}} = 24.5 \text{ g}/98 = 0.25 \text{ moles}$$

Therefore solution is 0.25 molar

$$H_2SO_4 \longrightarrow 2H^+ + SO_4^{2-}$$
$$0.25 \text{ m} \qquad\qquad 0.5 \text{ mole}$$

$$[H^+] = 0.5 \text{ mole/litre}$$
$$pH = -\log[H^+] = -\log[0.5] = 0.301$$

pH calculation for strong bases

Sample problem: Find the pH of a solution of 4 g of sodium hydroxide in 500 cm³ of solution

4 g in $500 \text{ cm}^3 = 8$ g in 1000 cm^3

$$\frac{\text{actual mass}}{\text{molar mass}} = 8/40 = 0.2 \text{ moles}$$

$$NaOH \longrightarrow Na^+ + OH^-$$
$$0.2 \text{ moles} \qquad\qquad 0.2 \text{ moles}$$

$$pOH = -\log[OH^-] = -\log[0.2] = .6989$$
$$pH + pOH = 14$$

Therefore: $pH = 14 - pOH = 14 - 0.6989 = 13.301$

Weak acids and weak bases

key definition

A weak acid or weak base is only slightly dissociated in aqueous solution.

Therefore when a weak acid or base dissociates in water it produces a relatively small number of ions in comparison to a strong acid or base.

Dissociation constants of weak acids and bases   (HL)

key definition

A dissociation constant of a weak acid or base is defined as the product of the concentration of the ions of the acid or base divided by the concentration of the acid or base itself.

(all concentrations measured in moles/litre)

Weak acids

Ethanoic acid is a weak acid and dissociates as follows.

$$CH_3COOH \rightleftharpoons CH_3COO^- + H^+$$

This is a reversible reaction as ethanoic acid is a weak acid and is therefore only slightly dissociated in aqueous solution. An equilibrium is set up when the rate of the forward reaction is equal to the rate of the reverse reaction.

The equilibrium constant is as follows:

$$K_a = \frac{[CH_3COO^-][H^+]}{[CH_3COOH]}$$

Note that the value for the K_a here is small indicating a lack of dissociation. The bigger the K_a the greater the dissociation into ions and the stronger the acid.

To establish a formula for weak acid calculations

If we cross multiply in the above expression we get:

$$[CH_3COO^-][H^+] = K_a[CH_3COOH]$$

But
$$[CH_3COO^-] = [H^+]$$

Therefore
$$[CH_3COO^-][H^+] = [H^+][H^+] = [H^+]^2$$
$$[H^+]^2 = K_a[CH_3COOH]$$

$$[H^+] = \sqrt{K_a[CH_3COOH]}$$

The above formula can be used as a starting point for exam calculations. Just replace the ethanoic acid with whatever acid is given in the question.

Sample exam question on weak acids: 2002 Q4(d)

Calculate the pH of a 0.01 M solution of ethanoic acid given that its $K_a = 1.8 \times 10^{-5}$ (6 marks)

Solution

Note the concentration of CH_3COOH can be taken as 0.01 as it is only slightly dissociated.
$$[H^+] = \sqrt{K_a[CH_3COOH]}$$
$$= \sqrt{1.8 \times 10^{-5} \times 0.01}$$
$$= 0.000424 \qquad \text{(3 marks)}$$
$$pH = -\log[H^+] = -\log(0.000424)$$
$$pH = 3.37 \qquad \text{(3 marks)}$$

More difficult problem on weak acids: 2003 Q 8(b) Higher level

A bottle of vinegar is labelled 6% (w/v) acetic acid (ethanoic acid). The dissociation constant, K_a, for ethanoic acid is 1.8×10^{-5}. Find the approximate pH of the vinegar solution. (12 marks)

Solution

6% (w/v) = 6 g in 100 cm^3 = 60 g/litre　　　　　　　　　　(3 marks)
Change to moles: 1 mole ethanoic acid = 60 g
$$60 \div 60 = 1 \text{ mole} \qquad\qquad\qquad (3 \text{ marks})$$
The concentration of acid is 1 mole/litre
$$[H^+] = \sqrt{K_a[CH_3COOH]}$$
$$= \sqrt{1.8 \times 10^{-5} \times 1}$$
$$= .00424 \qquad\qquad\qquad (3 \text{ marks})$$
$$pH = -\log[H^+] = -\log(.00424)$$
$$= 2.372 \qquad\qquad\qquad (3 \text{ marks})$$

Weak bases

Find the pH of a solution containing 1.7 g of ammonia (NH_3) in 500 cm^3 of water given that its $K_b = 1.7 \times 10^{-5}$.

Solution

1.7 g of ammonia in 500 cm^3 = 3.4 g in 1000 cm^3
convert to moles/litre. . .
$$1 \text{ mole of NH} = 17 \text{ g}$$
$$\frac{3.4}{17} = 0.2 \text{ moles/litre}$$
weak base formula similar to weak acid:
$$[OH^-] = \sqrt{K_b \times [base]}$$
$$= \sqrt{1.7 \times 10^{-5} \times 0.2}$$
$$= .00184$$
$$\Rightarrow pOH = -\log[OH]$$
$$= 2.734$$
as
$$pH = 14 - pOH$$
$$pH = 14 - 2.734 = 11.266$$

The ionic product of water

Water molecules self-ionise to a small extent as:
$$H_2O \rightleftharpoons H^+ + OH^- \qquad \Delta H = +$$
This is a reversible reaction and an equilibrium is set up. The higher the temperature, the more ions are formed as the forward reaction is endothermic. The equilibrium constant can be written as:
$$K_c = \frac{[H^+][OH^-]}{[H_2O]}$$
Thus :　　　　　$$K_c[H_2O] = [H^+][OH^-]$$
As very few water molecules dissociate, the product $K_c[H_2O]$ is constant and is called the K_w the ionic product of water.

The ionic product of water $K_w = [H^+][OH^-]$

Sample problem on ionic product

Find the pH of pure water at 25 °C if $K_w = 1 \times 10^{-14}$

Solution

$$K_w = [H^+][OH^-]$$

The concentration of H^+ ions is equal to concentration of OH^- ions in pure water i.e. $[H^+] = [OH^-]$

$$\text{Therefore } 1 \times 10^{-14} = [H^+]^2$$
$$[H^+] = 1 \times 10^{-7}$$
$$pH = -\log[H^+] = 7$$

The value of the K_w increases as the temperature increases as the ionisation of water is endothermic. It is important to note that pure water still remains neutral as the concentrations of H^+ and OH^- are still equal.

Indicators

An indicator is a solution of a weak acid or weak base that changes colour as the pH changes.

1. Indicators to know:

Indicator	Colour in acid	Colour in base	pH range	Suitable for
Litmus	red	blue	5–8	Strong acid/strong base e.g. HCl/NaOH
Methyl orange	red	yellow	3–5	Strong acid/weak base e.g. HCl/Na$_2$CO$_3$
Phenolphthalein	colourless	pink	8–10	Strong base/weak acid e.g. NaOH/CH$_3$COOH

Titration curves – Change of ph during a titration

When an acid is being titrated with an alkali, the pH increases during the process (alkali is being added). Normally a 0.1 M solution of the alkali is added to a 0.1 M solution of the acid so that the experiment starts with a low pH and rises slowly to a high pH.

Titration of strong acid and strong base

Procedure

In this titration the 25 cm³ of 0.1 M solution of NaOH is added slowly from a burette to a solution of 25 cm³ 0.1 M HCl in a beaker, adding very slowly when the end-point approaches. A magnetic stirrer is used to keep the solution mixed thoroughly and the pH meter gives readings for pH. A table of results is drawn up and a graph drawn.

Sodium hydroxide solution

pH meter

HCl solution

Apparatus to measure pH changes during a titration

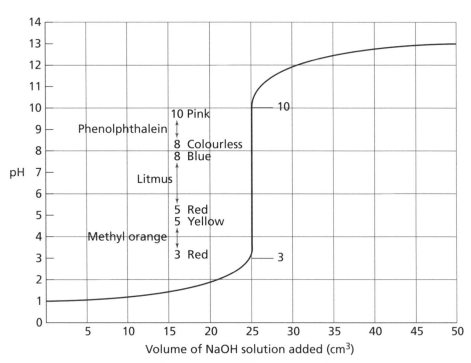

pH curve for a strong acid/strong base titration

It is noted from the graph that there is a sudden jump in pH at the end-point from about pH 3 to pH 10 and the vertical line on the graph demonstrates this.

When selecting an indicator for a titration you must know:

- the pH range of solution at end-point (where the alkali neutralises the acid)
- the pH range at which the indicator changes colour rapidly.

When titrating a strong acid (HCl) and a strong alkali (NaOH), most indicators are suitable since there is a large change in pH value at the end-point (from 3 to 10).

The changing point of indicator must appear on vertical line of graph showing great pH change for minimum amount (drop) of alkali added.

Therefore litmus or methyl orange or phenolphthalein indicators could be used for a strong acid–strong base titration as they all change colour between these values of pH.

Titration of a weak acid and a strong base: Ethanoic acid (CH₃COOH) and sodium hydroxide (NaOH)

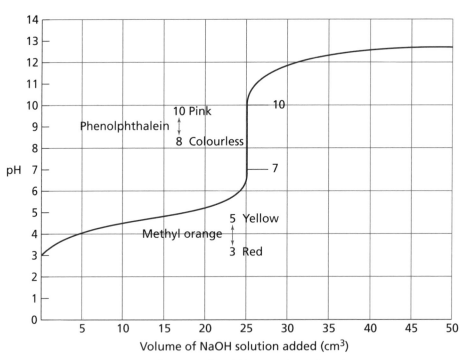

pH curve for a weak acid/strong base titration

When titrating a weak acid (CH₃COOH) and a strong base (NaOH) the jump in pH on the graph occurs in the pH range 7–10 so an indicator which changes colour in this range will suit e.g. phenolphthalein.

Titration of a strong acid and a weak base: Hydrochloric acid (HCl) and sodium carbonate (Na₂CO₃)

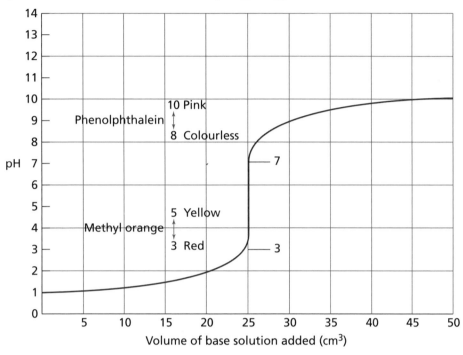

pH curve for a strong acid/weak base titration

As can be seen from the graph there is a large increase in the pH at the end-point from pH 3 to pH 7. Therefore methyl orange which changes colour in that pH range would suit this titration.

Titration of a weak acid and a weak base: Ethanoic acid (CH₃COOH) and sodium carbonate (Na₂CO₃)

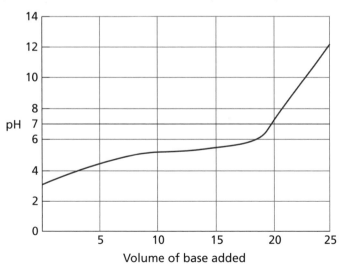

pH curve for a weak acid/weak base titration

In this titration there is no sharp change in pH at the end-point so there is no indicator to suit this type of titration.

Theory of acid/base indicators

Weak acid indicator

Consider the indicator to be a weak acid e.g. HIN. It would dissociate slightly in aqueous solution as follows.

$$HIN \rightleftharpoons H^+ + IN^-$$
red   blue

The undissociated acid (HIN) has a different colour to its conjugate base IN^-. If, for example, HIN is taken to be litmus then it is red whereas its conjugate base IN^- has a blue colour.

Case 1: if we add acid e.g. HCl

- This will increase the H^+ concentration.
- By Le Chatelier's principle the equilibrium shifts from right to left.
- This produces more HIN and the colour of HIN will prevail i.e. solution will be red for acid.

Case 2: adding base e.g. NaOH

- Reduces the concentration of H^+ ions as they will react with the OH^- ions from the base.
- Thus the equilibrium will move from left to right.
- This creates more IN^- ions and its colour will predominate i.e. the colour will be blue.

Weak base indicator

If the indicator is taken to be a weak base e.g. XOH

Methyl orange is an example of a weakly basic indicator which is yellow in an acid and red in a base.

It will dissociate slightly in aqueous solution as follows:

$$XOH \rightleftharpoons X^+ + OH^-$$
yellow   red

Case 1: if an acid is added:

- This will increase H^+ concentration and remove OH^- ions.
- Equilibrium will shift from left to right.
- More X^+ ions are created and the colour will be red.

Case 2: if a base is added:

- The concentration of OH^- ions increases.
- Equilibrium will shift from right to left.
- More of XOH is formed and so colour will be yellow.

13 Organic Chemistry 1

To revise the following:

- Alkanes: properties and reactions
- Free radical substitution of alkanes
- Chloroalkanes
- Alkenes
- Aromatic compounds e.g. benzene

What is organic chemistry?

Organic chemistry is the study of the compounds of carbon.

Compounds of carbon are divided into different families. Each family is called a homologous series.

key definition

Homologous series:

- group of compounds with the same general formula
- similar chemical properties
- successive members differ by CH_2.

First homologous series of hydrocarbons: The alkanes

Alkanes are hydrocarbons i.e. compounds of hydrogen and carbon only.

General formula of alkanes: C_NH_{2N+2} where n = 1, 2, 3... .

Naming the alkanes:

Number of carbons	Name	Molecular formula	Memory aid
1	Methane	CH_4	Make
2	Ethane	C_2H_6	Every
3	Propane	C_3H_8	Pupil
4	Butane	C_4H_{10}	Busy
5	Pentane	C_5H_{12}	Piling

Number of carbons	Name	Molecular formula	Memory aid
6	Hexane	C_6H_{14}	<u>H</u>uge
7	Heptane	C_7H_{16}	<u>H</u>omework
8	Octane	C_8H_{18}	<u>O</u>
9	Nonane	C_9H_{20}	<u>N</u>
10	Decane	$C_{10}H_{22}$	<u>D</u>aily

It is vital you remember the order here as the naming of the other homologous series follows this system.

To help you remember the order of the names in the tables try the mnemonic:

'Make every pupil busy piling huge homework on daily'.

Structure of alkanes

Alkanes are tetrahedral carbon compounds with the basic tetrahedral structure of methane repeated and joined by single covalent bonds.

The table below shows the structure of the first three alkanes.

Name	Molecular formula	Structural formula
Methane	CH_4	H | H—C—H | H Methane has one tetrahedral carbon
Ethane	C_2H_6	H H | | H—C—C—H | | H H Ethane has two tetrahedral carbons
Propane	C_3H_8	H H H | | | H—C—C—C—H | | | H H H Propane has three tetrahedral carbons

key definition

Molecular formula is the actual ratio of atoms in one molecule of a compound e.g. ethane (C_2H_6).

Structural formula is the spatial arrangement of atoms in one molecule of a compound.

General properties of the alkanes

- Lower members are gases, upper members are liquids and wax-like solids (methane, ethane, propane and butane are gases but pentane is a liquid).
- Being non-polar covalent compounds, they are not soluble in water because water is polar. They are soluble in non-polar organic solvents such as cyclohexane. It is important to remember the rule that 'like dissolves like' (a non-polar substance will dissolve in a non-polar liquid).
- Alkanes burn in oxygen to produce carbon dioxide and water vapour e.g. burning ethane in air:

$$C_2H_6 \ + \ 3\tfrac{1}{2}O_2 \ \longrightarrow \ 2CO_2 \ + \ 3H_2O$$
Ethane

- Alkanes are saturated compounds i.e. they consist of molecules with single bonds only between the carbon atoms.

Big reaction for alkanes

key definition

Substitution reactions of alkanes: In this type of reaction one or more atoms are replaced by another atom or group of atoms.

Substitution reaction of methane and chlorine

Overall reaction:

$$CH_4 \ + \ Cl_2 \ \xrightarrow{\text{uv light}} \ CH_3Cl \ + \ HCl$$
Methane   Chlorine   Chloromethane   Hydrogen chloride

The above reaction is not a one step reaction but goes through different stages. The mechanism for this reaction is called a free radical mechanism where a free radical is a species with an unpaired electron.

(HL)

Question: Outline the free radical mechanism for chlorination of methane

Solution

- Stage 1. Initiation

$$Cl\text{—}Cl \xrightarrow{\text{uv light}} Cl^{\cdot} + Cl^{\cdot}$$

The ultraviolet light provides the energy to break the covalent bond in the chlorine molecule creating two very reactive chlorine free radicals. The dot on the symbol for chlorine represents an unpaired electron.

- Stage 2. Propagation

The chlorine free radicals react with methane gas molecule as follows.

$$CH_4 + Cl^{\cdot} \longrightarrow CH_3^{\cdot} + HCl$$
$$\text{methyl free radical}$$
$$CH_3^{\cdot} + Cl_2 \longrightarrow CH_3Cl + Cl^{\cdot}$$
$$\text{chloromethane}$$

The free radical $Cl^{\cdot}$ is now ready to react with another CH_4 molecule and the process repeats.

- Stage 3. Termination

When the concentration of Cl_2 or CH_4 drops, the free radicals recombine and the reaction stops:

$$Cl^{\cdot} + Cl^{\cdot} \longrightarrow Cl_2$$
$$Cl^{\cdot} + CH_3^{\cdot} \longrightarrow CH_3Cl \text{ (chloroethane)}$$
$$CH_3^{\cdot} + CH_3^{\cdot} \longrightarrow C_2H_6 \text{ (ethane)}$$

Sample exam question: 2005 Q7(d) Higher level

State three pieces of experimental evidence for this mechanism. **(15 marks)**

Solution

- Reaction requires ultraviolet light to start. (5 marks)
- Ethane is formed. (5 marks)
- Addition of free radicals such as tetraethyllead speed up the reaction. (5 marks)

Exercise: Describe the free radical mechanism for the chlorination of ethane (also required for Leaving Certificate Higher level).

IUPAC naming of alkanes and structural isomers

Rules for naming alkanes:

- The longest continuous chain is taken as the parent alkane.
- If there are side groups they must be numbered.
- Side groups are numbered in such a way as to give the lowest number to the carbon with the side chain.

- When there are two side groups at the same carbon atom numbers must be given to each.
- Common side groups are methyl (CH_3), ethyl (C_2H_5), chloro (Cl), bromo (Br).

Sample exam question: 2005 Q6(b) Higher level   HL

There are three structural isomers of the alkane C_5H_{12}. In the case of each of these isomers draw the structure of the molecule and give its systematic IUPAC name.   (18 marks)

Solution

Structural isomers are different structural formulas for the same molecular formula.

(i) The first structural isomer here is pentane with the longest continuous chain of five carbons.

$$H—\overset{\overset{\displaystyle H}{|}}{\underset{\underset{\displaystyle H}{|}}{C}}—\overset{\overset{\displaystyle H}{|}}{\underset{\underset{\displaystyle H}{|}}{C}}—\overset{\overset{\displaystyle H}{|}}{\underset{\underset{\displaystyle H}{|}}{C}}—\overset{\overset{\displaystyle H}{|}}{\underset{\underset{\displaystyle H}{|}}{C}}—\overset{\overset{\displaystyle H}{|}}{\underset{\underset{\displaystyle H}{|}}{C}}—H$$

(3 marks for structure and 3 marks for correct name)

(ii) The second isomer has a longest chain of four carbons with a methyl side chain at carbon two.

$$H—\overset{\overset{\displaystyle H}{|}}{\underset{\underset{\displaystyle H}{|}}{C}}—\overset{\overset{\displaystyle H}{|}}{\underset{\underset{\displaystyle CH_3}{|}}{C}}—\overset{\overset{\displaystyle H}{|}}{\underset{\underset{\displaystyle H}{|}}{C}}—\overset{\overset{\displaystyle H}{|}}{\underset{\underset{\displaystyle H}{|}}{C}}—H \quad \text{(3 marks)}$$

IUPAC name is 2-methylbutane (3 marks)

(iii) The third isomer has a longest chain of three carbon atoms with two side groups of carbon two. Each side group is numbered and as there are two methyl groups the prefix *di-* is used.

$$H—\overset{\overset{\displaystyle H}{|}}{\underset{\underset{\displaystyle H}{|}}{C}}—\overset{\overset{\displaystyle CH_3}{|}}{\underset{\underset{\displaystyle CH_3}{|}}{C}}—\overset{\overset{\displaystyle H}{|}}{\underset{\underset{\displaystyle H}{|}}{C}}—H \quad \text{(3 marks)}$$

IUPAC name is 2, 2-dimethylpropane   (3 marks)

Chloroalkanes

key definition

Chloroalkanes are alkanes where one or more of the hydrogen atoms have been replaced by chlorine atoms. e.g. chloroethane (C_2H_5Cl).

Other examples of chloroalkanes are:

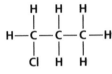

1-chloropropane

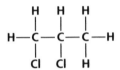

1, 2 dichloropropane

Properties of chloroalkanes

- Not soluble in water but soluble in non-polar solvents.
- Most chloroalkanes are liquids at room temperature.
- Chloroalkanes are used as solvents to remove oil, paint, grease etc.

Alkenes

Alkenes are a group of hydrocarbons that contain a double bond between two carbon atoms.

key definition

Unsaturated compounds contain at least one double or triple bond between carbon atoms.

Therefore alkenes are unsaturated as they contain a double bond.

key definition

Functional group: an atom or group of atoms that define the characteristic properties of a homologous series.

Functional group of alkenes is —C=C—.
General formula of alkenes is C_NH_{2N} where N = 2, 3...

Naming of alkenes

- Ethene is the first alkene and its molecular formula is C_2H_4:

Structure of ethene

Ethene has two planar carbons.

- Propene (C_3H_6)

Structure of propene:

Propene has two planar carbons and one tetrahedral carbon

Further IUPAC naming of alkenes

- The longest continuous chain containing the carbon–carbon double bond is taken as the parent alkene.
- The double bond position is given a number.
- Numbering starts from the end nearest the double bond.

Sample exam question: 2006 Q9(d) Higher level   HL

Draw the structures and give the systematic IUPAC names for two alkene isomers of C_4H_8. (12 marks)

Solution

(i) But-1-ene
    (3 marks)

$$H-\overset{\overset{\displaystyle H}{|}}{\underset{\underset{\displaystyle H}{|}}{C}}-\overset{\overset{\displaystyle H}{|}}{\underset{\underset{\displaystyle H}{|}}{C}}-\overset{\overset{\displaystyle H}{|}}{C}=\overset{\overset{\displaystyle H}{|}}{C}-H$$

Structure
(3 marks)

(ii) But-2-ene
     (3 marks)

$$H-\overset{\overset{\displaystyle H}{|}}{\underset{\underset{\displaystyle H}{|}}{C}}-\overset{\overset{\displaystyle H}{|}}{C}=\overset{\overset{\displaystyle H}{|}}{C}-\overset{\overset{\displaystyle H}{|}}{\underset{\underset{\displaystyle H}{|}}{C}}-H$$

Structure
(3 marks)

Preparation of alkenes

Alkenes can generally be prepared by the dehydration of alcohols i.e. where water is removed.

Ethene, for example, is prepared by the dehydration of ethanol as:

$$C_2H_5OH \xrightarrow{\;\;Al_2O_3\;\;} C_2H_4 + H_2O$$
$$\text{Ethanol} \quad \text{Heat}$$

Aluminium oxide (Al_2O_3) acts as a catalyst here.

key definition

Elimination reaction: The above reaction is an example of an elimination reaction where a small molecule (in this case water) is removed from a larger molecule leaving a double bond in the larger molecule.

Reaction of alkenes

- Combustion of alkenes: alkenes burn in oxygen to give carbon dioxide and water.
$$C_2H_4 + 3O_2 \longrightarrow 2CO_2 + 2H_2O$$
Ethene

Big reaction for alkenes: Addition reactions

Alkenes undergo addition reactions as they are unsaturated.

> **key definition**
>
> An addition reaction is where two molecules react and combine to form a larger molecule.

Example: Addition of hydrogen: (reduction or hydrogenation)
The addition of hydrogen to an alkene produces an alkane.

$$\text{Alkene} + \text{Hydrogen} \xrightarrow{\text{Ni/heat}} \text{Alkane}$$

$$C_2H_4 \quad + \quad H_2 \xrightarrow{\text{Ni/heat}} \quad C_2H_6$$
$$\text{Ethene} \qquad \text{Hydrogen} \qquad \text{Ethane}$$

Note that in this reaction there is a structural change from a planar carbon compound to a tetrahedral carbon compound. Structurally the reaction is:

$$
\begin{array}{c}
\text{H}\quad\text{H} \\
|\quad\ | \\
\text{C}=\text{C} + \text{H}-\text{H} \\
|\quad\ | \\
\text{H}\quad\text{H}
\end{array}
\xrightarrow{\text{Ni/heat}}
\begin{array}{c}
\text{H}\quad\text{H} \\
|\quad\ | \\
\text{H}-\text{C}-\text{C}-\text{H} \\
|\quad\ | \\
\text{H}\quad\text{H}
\end{array}
$$

Ethene   Ethane

2 planar carbons   2 tetrahedral carbons

Tests for unsaturation

There are two tests to show unsaturation i.e. presence of a double or triple bond.

Test 1

When bromine water is added to an unsaturated compound such as ethene there is a colour change from reddish brown to colourless.

$$C_2H_4 \quad + \quad Br_2 \quad \longrightarrow \quad C_2H_4Br_2$$
$$\text{Ethene} \qquad\quad \text{Bromine} \qquad\qquad \text{1, 2 dibromoethane}$$
$$\qquad\qquad\qquad \text{red/brown} \qquad\qquad\qquad \text{colourless}$$

Structurally this reaction is as follows:

$$
\begin{array}{c}
\text{H}\quad\text{H} \\
|\quad\ | \\
\text{C}=\text{C} + \text{Br}-\text{Br} \\
|\quad\ | \\
\text{H}\quad\text{H}
\end{array}
\longrightarrow
\begin{array}{c}
\text{H}\quad\text{H} \\
|\quad\ | \\
\text{H}-\text{C}-\text{C}-\text{H} \\
|\quad\ | \\
\text{Br}\quad\text{Br}
\end{array}
$$

Ethene   1, 2 Dibromoethane

Test 2

If an acidified solution of potassium manganate(VII) is added to an alkene it changes colour from purple to colourless.

Ionic addition mechanism for the addition of bromine to ethene

- Addition reactions are reactions where two substances react together to form a single substance. These reactions are typical of unsaturated compounds i.e. where there is a double or triple bond.
- The reaction of bromine with ethene is an example of an addition reaction. The overall reaction can be written as:

$$C_2H_4 \quad + \quad Br_2 \quad \longrightarrow \quad C_2H_4Br_2$$

Ethene $\qquad$ Bromine $\qquad$ 1, 2 dibromoethane

This reaction does not occur in one step but there are a number of stages that are outlined below.

Ionic addition mechanism for the addition of bromine to ethene   HL

Stage 1: The bromine molecule is polarised. When the bromine molecule approaches the highly negative area of the double bond, it is polarised into a partially positive bromine atom and a partially negative bromine atom as shown in the diagram.

- Bromine bond is polarised

Stage 2: The covalent bond between the bromine atoms breaks creating a positive Br^+ ion and negative Br^- ion.

- Bromine bond breaks forming Br^+ and Br^-. Br^+ attracted to C $=$ C double bond

Stage 3: The positive Br^+ ion now attacks the double bond and one of the double bonds break and the two electrons from this bond are used to form a new covalent bond with the Br^+ ion . This leaves one of the carbon atoms with a positive charge and it is called the carbonium ion.

- C $=$ C bond breaks, forming C^+ and a C $-$ Br bond. Br^- attracted to C^+

Stage 4: The negative bromine ion is attracted to the positive carbonium ion and forms a covalent bond with it. Therefore this explains why two Br atoms add on separately to different carbon atoms in this addition process.

- C $-$ Br bond formed

Ionic addition mechanism of bromine to ethene

Evidence for this mechanism

If bromine water containing sodium chloride is added to this reaction, extra products are formed due to the presence of other negative ions i.e. chloride ion Cl^- and hydroxyl ion OH^-.

- If the chloride ion adds on instead of the bromide ion 1-bromo-2-chloro ethane is formed.
- If OH^- ion adds on then 2-bromoethanol is formed.

The ionic addition mechanisms of HCl to ethene and Cl_2 to ethene are also required for the Leaving Certificate higher level exam. When HCl adds on H^+ and Cl^- ions are added and chloroethane is the product. When Cl_2 adds on Cl^- and Cl^+ ions are added and 1,2 dichloroethane is formed.

Polymerisation of alkenes

Polymerisation occurs when many small molecules called monomers are joined together to form a large molecule called a polymer.

Ethene is polymerised to form the important plastic called poly(ethene) which is used, for example, in plastic bags.

$$
\begin{array}{ccccc}
\underset{\underset{H}{|}}{\overset{\overset{H}{|}}{C}}=\underset{\underset{H}{|}}{\overset{\overset{H}{|}}{C}} & + & \underset{\underset{H}{|}}{\overset{\overset{H}{|}}{C}}=\underset{\underset{H}{|}}{\overset{\overset{H}{|}}{C}} & \xrightarrow[\text{Catalyst}]{\text{Heat, pressure}} & -\underset{\underset{H}{|}}{\overset{\overset{H}{|}}{C}}-\underset{\underset{H}{|}}{\overset{\overset{H}{|}}{C}}-\underset{\underset{H}{|}}{\overset{\overset{H}{|}}{C}}-\underset{\underset{H}{|}}{\overset{\overset{H}{|}}{C}}-
\end{array}
$$

Ethene   Ethene   Poly(ethene)

Manufacture of PVC (Polyvinyl chloride) from ethene

Stage 1: Production of chloroethene

$$\underset{\text{Ethene}}{C_2H_4} \ + \ Cl_2 \ \longrightarrow \ \underset{\text{1, 2 dichlorethane}}{CH_2Cl\!-\!CH_2Cl} \ \xrightarrow{\text{Heat}} \ \underset{\text{Chloroethene}}{CH_2CHCl}$$

Stage 2: Polymerisation of chloroethene

$$
\begin{array}{ccccc}
\underset{\underset{H}{|}}{\overset{\overset{H}{|}}{C}}=\underset{\underset{H}{|}}{\overset{\overset{Cl}{|}}{C}} & + & \underset{\underset{H}{|}}{\overset{\overset{H}{|}}{C}}=\underset{\underset{H}{|}}{\overset{\overset{Cl}{|}}{C}} & \xrightarrow[\text{Catalyst}]{\text{Heat, pressure}} & -\underset{\underset{H}{|}}{\overset{\overset{H}{|}}{C}}-\underset{\underset{H}{|}}{\overset{\overset{Cl}{|}}{C}}-\underset{\underset{H}{|}}{\overset{\overset{H}{|}}{C}}-\underset{\underset{H}{|}}{\overset{\overset{Cl}{|}}{C}}-
\end{array}
$$

Chloroethene Chloroethene   Poly(chloroethene) = PVC

Alkenes in general are used to make plastics.

Aliphatic and aromatic compounds

key definition

Aliphatic compounds consist of chains of carbon atoms either branched or unbranched as well as closed chains.

Aromatic compounds are compounds that contain the benzene ring.

Benzene (C_6H_6) is the most important aromatic compound and a small percentage of it is used in petrol to increase the octane number of petrol and make it burn more efficiently. It is carcinogenic (cancer causing).

Structure of benzene **HL**

- It was once thought that alternate double and single bonds existed between the carbon atoms in the benzene ring.
- Accurate measurements of bond length in the benzene molecule have shown that all the bond lengths are the same indicating that alternate single and double bonds do not exist.

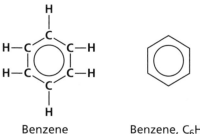

Benzene   Benzene, C_6H_6

- Benzene is now described as having an intermediate type of bond (intermediate in length between a double and a single bond).
- Each carbon is joined to two neighbouring carbons and one hydrogen by sigma bonds ('head on' overlap of orbitals with two electrons shared).
- The remaining electron on each carbon atom is given to a pi bond where the electrons are free to move and are shared equally by the carbon atoms in the ring. This pi bond is represented by a circle, as shown in the diagram. Marks will be lost if this is omitted from the diagram.

Other aromatic compounds to know

- Methylbenzene, which is also known as toluene (C_7H_8) has the following structure.

  Toluene is used as an industrial solvent or in explosives as trinitrotoluene (TNT).

Methylbenzene, C_7H_8 (toluene)

- Ethylbenzene (C_7H_{10}) has the structure shown on the right.
- Aspirin is an aromatic compound.
- The acid-base indicators methyl orange and phenolphthalein are aromatic.

Ethylbenzene, C_8H_{10}

14 Organic Chemistry 2

 To revise the following
- Alcohols
- Aldehydes
- Ketones
- Organic acids and esters
- Solubility and boiling points of the various homologous series

Alcohols

- Alcohols have general formula ROH where R = CH_3, C_2H_5 etc.
- General formula: $C_N H_{2N+1}OH$.
- Functional group: the hydroxyl group: $OH(-O-H)$.
- Alcohols are named by replacing the –e at the end of the corresponding alkane with an –ol e.g. methanol is the first alcohol.
- Alcohols have a tetrahedral structure like the alkanes.

Naming alcohols

- The longest continuous chain containing the OH group is taken as the parent alcohol.
- The position of the OH group is given a number.
- Numbering of side groups start from the end nearest the OH group.

The first two alcohols are methanol (CH_3OH) and ethanol (C_2H_5OH). Their structures are:

$$H-\overset{\overset{\displaystyle H}{|}}{\underset{\underset{\displaystyle H}{|}}{C}}-O-H$$

Methanol

$$H-\overset{\overset{\displaystyle H}{|}}{\underset{\underset{\displaystyle H}{|}}{C}}-\overset{\overset{\displaystyle H}{|}}{\underset{\underset{\displaystyle H}{|}}{C}}-O-H$$

Ethanol

The third alcohol propanol (C_3H_7OH) can exist as two structural isomers:

$$H-\overset{\overset{\displaystyle H}{|}}{\underset{\underset{\displaystyle H}{|}}{C}}-\overset{\overset{\displaystyle H}{|}}{\underset{\underset{\displaystyle H}{|}}{C}}-\overset{\overset{\displaystyle H}{|}}{\underset{\underset{\displaystyle H}{|}}{C}}-O-H$$

Propan-1-ol
(primary alcohol)

$$H-\overset{\overset{\displaystyle H}{|}}{\underset{\underset{\displaystyle H}{|}}{C}}-\overset{\overset{\displaystyle H}{|}}{\underset{\underset{\displaystyle OH}{|}}{C}}-\overset{\overset{\displaystyle H}{|}}{\underset{\underset{\displaystyle H}{|}}{C}}-H$$

Propan-2-ol
(secondary alcohol)

Primary and secondary alcohols

- Primary alcohol: where there is one carbon attached to the carbon with the OH group e.g. propan-1-ol or 1-propanol
- Secondary alcohol: where there are two carbons attached to the carbon with the OH group e.g. propan-2-ol
- Tertiary alcohol: where there are three carbons attached to the carbon with the OH group. e.g. 2-methyl propan-2-ol

$$H-\underset{\underset{H}{|}}{\overset{\overset{H}{|}}{C}}-\underset{\underset{OH}{|}}{\overset{\overset{CH_3}{|}}{C}}-\underset{\underset{H}{|}}{\overset{\overset{H}{|}}{C}}-H$$

Preparation of alcohol

General preparation of alcohols: Alkene   +   Water   =   Alcohol
Ethanol can be prepared from ethene by adding water as follows:

$$C_2H_4 \;+\; H_2O \;\longrightarrow\; C_2H_5OH$$
$$\text{Ethene} \qquad\qquad\qquad \text{Ethanol}$$

Reactions of alcohols

- Oxidation of a primary alcohol gives an aldehyde and further oxidation gives an acid.
- The oxidising agent for both oxidations is mixture of sodium dichromate and sulfuric acid. During the oxidation the sodium dichromate changes colour from orange to green as the chromium ion is being reduced from the $+6$ state to the green $+3$ state.

$$\text{Primary Alcohol} \;\xrightarrow{[O]}\; \text{Aldehyde} \;\xrightarrow{[O]}\; \text{Acid}$$

Examples of oxidation

1. $CH_3OH \xrightarrow{[O]} HCHO \xrightarrow{[O]} HCOOH$
   Methanol   Methanal   Methanoic acid

2. $C_2H_5OH \xrightarrow{[O]} CH_3CHO \xrightarrow{[O]} CH_3COOH$
   Ethanol   Ethanal   Ethanoic acid

Oxidation of primary and secondary alcohols

It is important to note that the oxidation of a primary alcohol gives an aldehyde but the oxidation of a secondary alcohol gives a ketone.

Example

The oxidation of the primary alcohol 1-propanol gives propanal and further oxidation gives propanoic acid:

$$CH_3CH_2CH_2OH \xrightarrow{[O]} C_2H_5CHO \xrightarrow{[O]} C_2H_5COOH$$

    1-propanol   Propanal   Propanoic acid

The oxidation of the secondary alcohol, 2-propanol, however, gives the ketone propanone only:

$$CH_3CHOHCH_3 \xrightarrow{[O]} CH_3COCH_3$$

    2-propanol   Propanone

Note that the oxidising agent for both reactions is acidified sodium dichromate.

Reaction of alcohols with sodium

This reaction demonstrates the acidic nature of alcohols.

$$C_2H_5OH + Na \longrightarrow C_2H_5ONa + \tfrac{1}{2}H_2$$

    Ethanol   Sodium   Sodium   Hydrogen
                              ethoxide   gas

The hydrogen gas released in this reaction can be tested by showing that when lit, hydrogen forms an explosive mixture with air.

Esterification reaction of alcohols

> **The reaction of an organic acid and an alcohol to form an ester and water is called an esterification reaction.**

It is regarded as a substitution reaction where the OH group of the acid is replaced by the alcohol. Water is formed as a byproduct.

$$C_2H_5OH + CH_3COOH \xrightarrow{H_2SO_4} CH_3COOC_2H_5 + H_2O$$

    Ethanol   Ethanoic acid   Ethyl ethanoate   Water

This reaction is catalysed by adding dilute sulfuric acid.

Uses of alcohols

- As an alcoholic drink: Ethanol is made in industry from the fermentation of sugar using yeast for use in beers, wine and spirits like whiskey.

$$C_6H_{12}O_6 \xrightarrow{\text{Yeast}} 2C_2H_5OH + 2CO_2$$

Glucose   Ethanol   Carbon dioxide

- As a solvent: Ethanol is widely used as a solvent in paint and perfumes for example as both polar and non-polar solutes are soluble in it.
- As a fuel: Ethanol and methanol act as oxygenates i.e. can be added to motor fuel to raise the octane number.

Aldehydes

- General formula: RCHO where R = H, CH_3, C_2H_5 etc.
- Functional group: -CHO
- Naming of aldehydes is achieved by replacing the -e at the end of an alkane with -al. The first three aldehydes are; methanal (HCHO), ethanal (CH_3CHO) and propanal (C_2H_5CHO)

Preparation of aldehydes

Aldehydes are generally prepared by the oxidation of primary alcohols using acidified sodium dichromate.

Primary Alcohol $\xrightarrow{\text{[O]}}$ Aldehyde

$$C_2H_5OH \xrightarrow{\text{[O]}} CH_3CHO$$

Ethanol   Acidified sodium   Ethanal
dichromate
$(Na_2Cr_2O_7 + H_2SO_4)$

Ethanol   Ethanal

There is a structural change from two tetrahedral carbon atoms in ethanol to one tetrahedral and one planar carbon in ethanal.

Reactions of aldehydes e.g. ethanal (CH_3CHO)

- Aldehydes can be oxidized to organic acids using acidified sodium dichromate as an oxidising agent.

$$CH_3CHO \xrightarrow{\text{[O]}} CH_3COOH$$

Ethanal   Acidified   Ethanoic acid

sodium

Dichromate

- Aldehydes can be reduced to alcohols.

$$CH_3CHO \xrightarrow[\text{Heat}]{H_2/\text{Nickel}} C_2H_5OH$$

Ethanal   Heat   Ethanol

It is important to note as a memory aid that reduction is the opposite reaction to oxidation.

Tests to distinguish aldehydes from ketones and organic acids

Test 1: With Fehling's solution

Ease of oxidation of aldehydes can be shown by the fact that they reduce Fehlings solution. Fehling's solution consists of equal amounts of Fehling's 1 [a solution of copper(II) sulphate ($CuSO_4$)] and Fehling's 2 [potassium sodium tartrate].

Detail of test

1. To a solution of an aldehyde e.g. ethanal add equal amounts of Fehling's solutions 1 and Fehling's solution 2. The resultant solution has a deep blue colour.
2. Warm the solution by putting test tube in a beaker of hot water.
3. Fehling's solution changes colour from deep blue producing a a brick-red precipitate. The aldehyde is oxidised to the acid.

Test 2: With Tollens' reagent

Tollens reagent consists of a solution of silver nitrate in ammonia.

Detail of test

1. Add a few drops of aldehyde to Tollens' reagent in a clean test tube.
2. Warm the test tube by placing in a beaker of hot water.

3. Silver is deposited on the wall of the test tube in the form of a mirror. This is why this test is often called the silver mirror test.

Representative reaction:

$$CH_3CHO \quad + \quad Ag_2O \quad \longrightarrow \quad CH_3COOH \quad + \quad 2Ag$$

| Ethanal | Silver oxide in ammonia | Ethanoic acid | Silver |

In the above reaction the aldehyde is oxidised to the acid and silver oxide is reduced to silver. (Ag^+ to Ag).

Note: If a ketone or organic acid was used in either of the above tests there would be no colour change as neither compounds are easily oxidised.

Occurrence of aldehydes

The aromatic aldehyde, benzaldehyde (C_6H_5CHO), is found in the oil of almonds and contributes to the flavour of the fruit. This is the only aromatic aldehyde you need to know on this course.

Ketones

- General formula:

$$
\begin{array}{c}
R \\
\diagdown \\
C{=}O \quad \text{where } R = \text{alkyl group e.g. } CH_3 \\
\diagup \\
R
\end{array}
$$

The alkyl groups may be the same or different.

- Functional group: $\begin{array}{c} \diagdown \\ C{=}O \\ \diagup \end{array}$ (the carbonyl group)

- Naming of ketones is achieved by replacing the -e at the end of an alkane with -one. The first two members of the ketones are:
  1. Propanone (CH_3COCH_3) and 2. Butanone ($C_2H_5COCH_3$)

Structure of propanone

The structural formulas of propanone and butanone are as follows:

Propanone   Butanone

Preparation of ketones

Oxidation of secondary alcohols using acidified sodium dichromate gives a ketone e.g. preparation of propanone:

$$CH_3CHOHCH_3 \xrightarrow{\substack{\text{Acidified} \\ \text{sodium dichromate}}} CH_3COCH_3$$

2-propanol   Propanone

Propan-2-ol   Propanone

Note there is a structural change here from three tetrahedral carbons to two tetrahedral carbons and one planar carbon.

Reaction of ketone

Reduction of ketones back to secondary alcohols:

$$CH_3COCH_3 \xrightarrow[\text{Heat}]{H_2/Ni} CH_3CHOHCH_3$$

Propanone   Heat   2-propanol

To distinguish aldehydes and ketones

Aldehydes are easily oxidised to organic acids but ketones are not. Therefore ketones are not oxidised by either Fehlings solution or Tollens reagent.

Uses of propanone

- Used in nail varnish remover.
- Used in solvents.

Carboxylic acids

- General formula: RCOOH where $R = H$, CH_3, C_2H_5 etc.
- Functional group: the carboxyl group -COOH
- Naming of carboxylic acids is achieved by replacing the -e of the corresponding alkane with -oic. The first four acids are:
  Methanoic (HCOOH), ethanoic (CH_3COOH), propanoic acid (C_2H_5COOH) and butanoic (C_3H_7COOH).

Naming and structure of carboxylic acids

- The longest continuous chain containing the COOH group is taken as the parent acid.
- Numbering of side groups starts from the end nearest the COOH group.

The structures of methanoic, ethanoic and propanoic acids are:

| Methanoic acid | Ethanoic acid | Propanoic acid |

Preparation of organic acids

Organic acids are prepared by the strong oxidation of the primary alcohol using acidified sodium dichromate as the oxidising agent.

$$\text{Primary Alcohol} \xrightarrow{[O]} \text{Aldehyde} \xrightarrow{[O]} \text{Acid}$$

Example: $C_2H_5OH \xrightarrow{[O]} CH_3CHO \xrightarrow{[O]} CH_3COOH$

   Ethanol   Ethanal   Ethanoic acid

Reactions of carboxylic acids

- Carboxylic acids react with sodium and magnesium metals to form salts and release hydrogen gas.

  (i) Reaction with sodium:

   $$CH_3COOH \ + \ Na \ \longrightarrow \ CH_3COONa \ + \ \tfrac{1}{2}H_2$$
   Sodium ethanoate

  (ii) Reaction with magnesium:

   $$2CH_3COOH \ + \ Mg \ \longrightarrow \ (CH_3COO)_2Mg \ + \ H_2$$
   Magnesium ethanoate

- Carboxylic acids react with bases to form salts:

  Reaction with sodium carbonate forms salt and water and carbon dioxide is released:

   $$2CH_3COOH \ + \ Na_2CO_3 \ \longrightarrow \ 2CH_3COONa \ + \ H_2O \ + \ CO_2$$
   Sodium ethanoate

- Reaction with alcohols to form esters:

   $$C_2H_5OH \ + \ C_2H_5COOH \xrightarrow{H_2SO_4} C_2H_5COOC_2H_5 \ + \ H_2O$$
   Propanoic acid   Ethyl propanoate

- Reduction of carboxylic acids to alcohols:

  This reaction is the reverse of the preparation.

   $$CH_3COOH \xrightarrow[\text{Heat}]{Ni/H_2} C_2H_5OH$$

Uses of carboxylic acids

- Methanoic acid is used in the stings of ants and nettles.
- Ethanoic acid is used in vinegar.
- Propanoic and benzoic acid are used as food preservatives.

(HL) Esters

- General formula RCOOR′ where R = H, CH_3, C_2H_5 etc. and R′ = CH_3, C_2H_5 etc.
- Functional group: COO
- In naming an ester name the alkyl group at the end of the molecule first and then name the acid from which it is derived. The acid part of the name changes from *-oic* to *-oate*.

Naming and structures of some esters

- $CH_3COOC_2H_5$ is called ethyl ethanoate as it is derived from ethanoic acid. Its structure is:

Ethyl ethanoate

- $HCOOCH_3$ is called methyl methanoate as it is derived from methanoic acid. Its structure is:

Methyl methanoate

Preparation of esters

Esters are prepared by the reaction of an organic acid and an alcohol. It is regarded as a substitution reaction where the OH group of the acid is replaced by the alcohol. Water is formed as a byproduct.

$$C_2H_5OH \ + \ CH_3COOH \ \xrightarrow{H_2SO_4} \ CH_3COOC_2H_5 \ + \ H_2O$$

Ethanol   Ethanoic acid   Ethyl ethanoate   Water

This reaction is catalysed by adding dilute sulfuric acid.

Occurrence and uses of esters

- Esters have strong pleasant fruity smells. They are found naturally in flowers and fruits.
- Fats and oils are esters that occur in nature.
- Esters are used in soap making and as solvents for glues.

Solubility and boiling points of the various homologous series

Solubility in water

- Hydrocarbons like alkanes and alkenes are non-polar and are therefore not soluble in water as water is polar. They are soluble in non-polar solvents such as cyclohexane.
- Alcohols are soluble in polar and non-polar solvents as their molecules contain the polar $O^{\sigma(-)} - H^{\delta(+)}$ group and a non-polar hydrocarbon part.
- Lower members of the aldehydes, ketones and esters are all soluble in water due to hydrogen bonding between the polar carbonyl group $C^{\delta(+)} = O^{\delta(-)}$ and water:

Note that the higher members of aldehydes, esters and ketones are not as soluble in water because the hydrocarbon part of the molecule which is non-polar is getting progressively larger.

- Carboxylic acids are soluble in water because of hydrogen bonding between their molecules and water.

exam focus

Memory aid: Alkanes and alkenes are not soluble in water but alcohols, aldehydes, ketones and acids are soluble due to hydrogen bonding.

Boiling points

- Alkanes and alkenes have low boiling points as the molecules are easy to separate on heating as only weak Van der Waal forces exist between the molecules.
- Aldehydes, esters and ketones have higher boiling points than hydrocarbons of similar mass as they have dipole-dipole attraction between their molecules due to the polar carbonyl group:

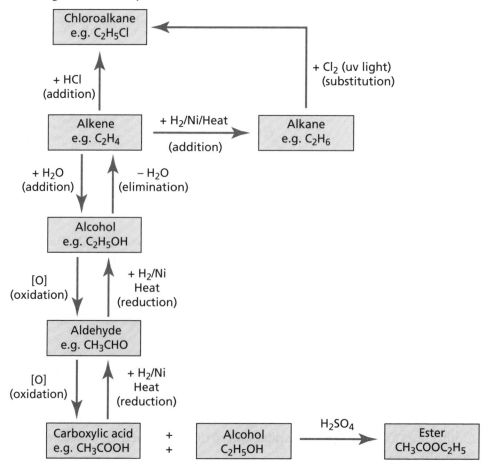

- Alcohols have higher boiling points than aldehydes or ketones as they have strong hydrogen bonding between their molecules.
- Carboxylic acids have higher boiling points than alcohols with similar mass as the have a greater amount of hydrogen bonding.

Summary of organic synthetic routes

The summary guide below is very useful to form links between the various homologous series in organic chemistry:

15 Fuels and Hydrocarbons

 aims To revise the following:
- Heats of reaction and bond energy
- Heats of combustion and formation
- Hess's law and problems
- Experiment to measure heat of reaction
- Oil refining and octane number
- Methods of increasing octane number

Heat of reaction

key definition

Heat of reaction (ΔH) is the heat change in kilojoules when the number of moles of reactants in the balanced equation for a particular reaction reacts completely.

An exothermic reaction occurs when heat is given out to the surroundings. Burning methane in oxygen is an example of an exothermic reaction.

$$CH_4 + 2O_2 \longrightarrow CO_2 + 2H_2O \qquad \Delta H = -484 \text{ kJ/mole}$$

Note that the heat of reaction (ΔH) is negative for an exothermic reaction.

An endothermic reaction occurs where heat is taken in. An example of an endothermic reaction is the heat taken in to break one mole of water into hydrogen gas and oxygen gas.

$$H_2O \longrightarrow H_2 + \tfrac{1}{2}O_2 \qquad \Delta H = +286 \text{ kJ/mole}$$

Note that the heat of reaction (ΔH) is positive for an endothermic reaction.

Bond energy

key definition

Bond energy is the average energy required to break one mole of covalent bonds and to separate the atoms completely from each other in the gaseous state.

In chemical reactions, energy must be supplied to break bonds and energy released when bonds are formed.

Example

In the reaction $CH_4 + 2O_2 \longrightarrow CO_2 + 2H_2O$ $\quad \Delta H = -484 \, kJ/mole$, list the bonds broken and the bonds formed and explain in terms of bond energy why the overall reaction is exothermic.

| These bonds are broken. Energy is taken in. | These bonds are made. Energy is given out. |

Bond energy

As there is greater amount of energy released in forming bonds than there is in breaking them, the overall reaction is exothermic.

The heat change for the breaking of the four covalent bonds in methane into its individual atoms is 1664 kJ/mole and can be represented by the reaction:

$$CH_{4(g)} \longrightarrow C_{(g)} + 4H_{(g)} \qquad \Delta H = \quad +1664 \, kJ/mole$$

Therefore the energy of a single $C-H$ bond

$$E(C-H) = 1664 \div 4 = 416 \, kJ/mole$$

The energy of a particular bond can vary depending on the molecule the bond is in.

Heat of combustion

Heat of combustion is the heat given out in kilojoules when 1 mole of a compound is burned in excess oxygen.

Example

Burning ethane in oxygen produces carbon dioxide and water.

$$C_2H_6 \; + \; 3\tfrac{1}{2}O_2 \; \longrightarrow \; 2CO_2 \; + \; 3H_2O \qquad \Delta H = -350 \, KJ/mole$$
$$\text{Ethane}$$

The above reaction tells us that when 1 mole of ethane (30 g) is burned in excess oxygen 350 kilojoules of heat is released.

Bomb calorimeter

Heat of combustion values can be measured very accurately using a bomb calorimeter. The basic principle of the method is that a measured mass of the substance is electrically burned under very controlled conditions and the heat released measured without loss of heat to surroundings.

- The fuel or food material is weighed accurately and placed in the calorimeter as shown and the lid is screwed on.
- Oxygen is forced in under pressure. The bomb is placed in a container of water and the initial temperature is recorded. The ignition wires are heated electrically and the fuel is set alight.
- The heat released by the burning fuel is absorbed by the water in the insulated steel container. The rise in temperature of the water is noted and this is used to calculate the amount of heat released from the fuel or food.
- This is then used to calculate the heat of combustion.

Bomb calorimeter

Kilogram calorific value

Kilogram calorific value is the heat given out when one kilogram of a substance is burned in excess oxygen.

This is a bigger unit than heat of combustion and is used by heat engineers, for example, to compare heat output of different fuels and to determine the size of boiler needed to heat a house or building.

Heat of formation HL

Heat of formation is the heat change in kilojoules which occurs when 1 mole of a compound is formed from its elements in their standard states.

Example

Write the heat of formation reaction for:
(i) ethane (C_2H_6) and (ii) ethanol.
N.B. In writing these reactions, elements must be used.
(i) $2C + 3H_2 \longrightarrow C_2H_6$ (ethane)
(ii) $2C + 3H_2 + \frac{1}{2}O_2 \longrightarrow C_2H_5OH$ (ethanol)

Law of conservation of energy
Energy cannot be created or destroyed but can be changed from one form into another.

Hess's law

Except in a few cases, heats of formation cannot be measured directly. However, heats of formation can be calculated from heats of combustion (which are very accurate) using Hess's law.

key definition

Hess's law states that the heat change for a given reaction depends on the initial and final states of the system and is independent of the path followed.

Sample problem on Hess's law

2006 Q6(c) Higher level

The combustion of cyclohexane can be described by the following balanced equation.

$$C_6H_{12} + 9O_2 \longrightarrow 6CO_2 + 6H_2O$$

Given that the heats of formation of cyclohexane, carbon dioxide and water are -156, -394 and -286 kJ/mole respectively, calculate the heat of combustion of cyclohexane.

(12 marks)

Solution

Step 1: First write the heat of formation reactions.

1. Cyclohexane: $6C + 6H_2 \longrightarrow C_6H_{12}$ $\Delta H = -156$ kJ/mole
2. Carbon dioxide: $C + O_2 \longrightarrow CO_2$ $\Delta H = -394$ kJ/mole
3. Water: $H_2 + \frac{1}{2}O_2 \longrightarrow H_2O$ $\Delta H = -286$ kJ/mole

Step 2: Write the reaction needed.

$$C_6H_{12} + 9O_2 \longrightarrow 6CO_2 + 6H_2O$$

Step 3: Combine the three reactions given to get the reaction needed.

Reverse reaction 1: $C_6H_{12} \longrightarrow 6C + 6H_2$ $\Delta H = 156$ kJ/mole   (3 marks)
Reaction 2 × 6: $6C + 6O_2 \longrightarrow 6CO_2$ $\Delta H = -2364$ kJ/mole   (3 marks)
Reaction 3 × 6: $6H_2 + 3O_2 \longrightarrow 6H_2O$ $\Delta H = -1716$ kJ/mole   (3 marks)
$C_6H_{12} + 9O_2 \longrightarrow 6CO_2 + 6H_2O$ $\Delta H = -3924$ kJ/mole   (3 marks)

Mandatory experiment: To determine the heat of reaction of hydrochloric acid and sodium hydroxide

Hydrochloric acid and sodium hydroxide neutralise each other and the reaction is exothermic. In the following experiment the heat released from this reaction will be measured. The equation for the reaction is shown.

$$HCl + NaOH \longrightarrow NaCl + H_2O$$

Procedure

- Using graduated cylinders measure out 50 cm³ of 1 M HCl and 50 cm³ of 1 M NaOH into separate polystyrene cups. The plastic polystyrene is used as it is a good insulator.

- Measure the temperature of each solution with a thermometer with an accuracy of 0.1 °C. If the temperatures of the two solutions don't match get an average temperature. Call this temperature T_1.

- Add one solution to the other and place the lid on the cup and stir the solution well. Record the highest temperature T_2. Note the rise in temperature which is $T_2 - T_1$.

- As the solutions are dilute the total mass of the solution can be taken as 100 g = 0.1 Kg (density of water = 1 g/cm³)

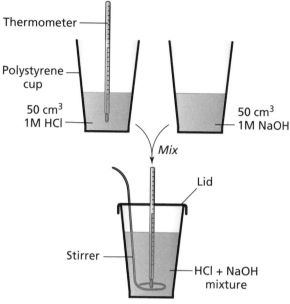

Measuring the heat of neutralisation of hydrochloric acid and sodium hydroxide

Sample problem and solution

When 50 cm³ of 1 M HCl and 50 cm³ of 1 M NaOH were mixed in a plastic container the rise in temperature was recorded at 6.7 °C.

(The specific heat capacity of the solution is 4200 J/Kg/K)

Find (i) the heat lost by the solution

(ii) the number of moles of acid neutralised

(iii) the heat of reaction.

Solution

(i) Heat loss by solution = Mass (in kg) × specific heat capacity × rise in temperature

$$= 0.1 \times 4200 \times 6.7$$
$$= 420 \times 6.7 = 2814\,J$$

Note that the total heat capacity (mass × specific heat) i.e. $420\ JK^{-1}$ could be given in the question.

(ii) Number of moles = molarity × volume in litres

$$= 1 \times 0.05 = 0.05 \text{ moles}$$

(iii) 0.05 moles HCl produces 2814 kJ

1 mole produces $2814 \div 0.05 = 56280\,J$

Therefore heat of reaction = 56280 J/mole

$$= 56.28 \text{ kJ/mole}$$

Oil refining, its products and their uses

Crude oil or petroleum can be separated into a number of useful parts called fractions in a process known as fractional distillation.

Fractional distillation is where a mixture, in this case crude oil, is separated by a process of boiling and condensing.

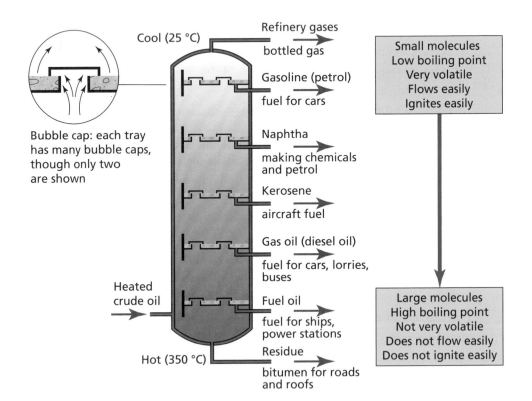

Fractional distillation

The main principle of this method is that each fraction in the crude oil is separated according to its boiling point.

The boiling of the crude oil is carried out in a fractionating column as shown in the diagram. The temperature is highest at the bottom where the crude oil is evaporated and fed in as a mixture of gases into the fractionating column. The temperature in the column decreases as the vapours move upwards. At different levels there are trays which contain many bubble caps which condense some of the gases into liquids and the liquids are then removed from the tower as fractions.

Fractions in crude oil and their uses

Fraction	Boiling point	No. of carbon atoms per molecule	Uses
Refinery gas	300 K (27 °C)or less	C1–C4 e.g. methane, ethane, propane and butane.	Bottled gas or liquid petroleum gas (LPG)
Light gasoline (petrol)	300–350 K (27–77 °C)	C5–C8	Petrol
Naphtha	350–435 K	C8–C10	Petrol
Kerosene	435–525 K	C10–C14	Central heating fuel
Gas oil (diesel)	525-625 K	C14–C19	Fuel for cars and trucks
Residue	>625 K	>C19	Bitumen for roads, lubricating oil

Refinery gas and natural gas

- Refinery gas, also called petroleum gas, consists of methane, ethane, propane and butane. Bottled gas is a mixture of propane and butane and is liquefied under pressure and is therefore called liquid petroleum gas (LPG).
- Natural gas is different to bottled gas in that it is mainly methane. Methane is an excellent fuel as it has a high energy output and burns cleanly.
- Both these gases are odourless and therefore mercaptans (sulfur compounds) are added to the gases to make them smell so that gas leaks can be detected.

Octane number and fuel efficiency

key definition

Octane number is the measure of the tendency of a fuel to resist knocking.

- Knocking is caused by auto-ignition i.e. early explosion of the petrol/air mixture in a car which can cause the engine to lose power. The petrol/air mix should only explode when ignited by the spark plug and efficient burning of the fuel then occurs.
- The efficiency of a fuel is measured by its low tendency to auto-ignite. The higher the octane number, the more efficient the fuel.
- 2,2,4-trimethylpentane has an octane number of 100 and is a most efficient fuel. Heptane, in contrast, is very inefficient and has an octane number of zero.

Structural factors affecting octane number

It has been shown by research that:

- the shorter the chain, the higher the octane number and the more efficient the fuel
- the more branched the chain, the higher the octane number.

As an example to demonstrate the above, octane has a much lower octane number than 2,2,4-trimethylpentane even though they have the same molecular formula (C_8H_{18}) and are therefore isomers of each other.

Octane

2, 2, 4-trimethylpentane

As 2,2,4-trimethylpentane has a short chain with three side groups it has an octane number of 100 as it burns very efficiently as a fuel. By contrast, octane has a long chain and has therefore a low octane number and is an inefficient fuel.

Hydrocarbons with small molecules make better fuels than hydrocarbons with large molecules as they are volatile, flow easily and are easily ignited.

- Cyclic compounds have a higher octane number than straight chain compounds, e.g. hexane has an octane number of 25 while cyclohexane has an octane number of 83.

Hexane
Octane number = 25

Cyclohexane
Octane number = 83

Cyclic compounds have a higher octane number than straight-chain compounds

Making petrol

Lead compounds like tetraethyllead were added to petrol in the past to reduce knocking. However, lead compounds are not used today as (i) they are toxic and (ii) they poison the catalyst in the catalytic converters in modern cars. Unleaded petrol is now used. Since the phasing out of lead, scientists have had to devise methods to increase the octane number of petrol. There are four main methods to increase octane number:

1. Isomerism: changing long straight chain hydrocarbons into shorter branched-chain ones using heat and catalysts. For example, pentane with an octane number of 62 can be converted using heat and a catalyst into 2-methylbutane with an octane number of 93.

2. Catalytic cracking: breakdown of long-chain hydrocarbons into more useful short-chain hydrocarbons thus increasing the octane number e.g. long-chain hydrocarbons like dodecane ($C_{12}H_{26}$) can be broken down into short-chain alkanes for fuel and short-chain alkenes for plastics.

3. Reforming (Dehydrocyclisation): this is where catalysts are used to form ring compounds. This process involves the removal of hydrogen and this is why it is called dehydrocyclisation. Alkanes are converted into cycloalkanes e.g. hexane is converted into cyclohexane. Also cycloalkanes can be converted into aromatic compounds (compounds of benzene).

4. Adding oxygenates: an oxygenate is a fuel that contains oxygen in its compounds. The oxygenates commonly added to petrol are methanol, ethanol and MTBE (methyl tertiary-butyl ether). The advantages of adding oxygenates to petrol are:

- they increase the octane number
- they give rise to very little pollution when they are burned.

Hydrogen as a fuel

Hydrogen is used in rocket fuel. The reaction for the burning of hydrogen in oxygen is shown:

$$H_2 + \tfrac{1}{2}O_2 \longrightarrow H_2O \text{ (steam)}$$

As water is the only byproduct of the reaction, the burning of hydrogen as a fuel is environmentally friendly. However as it forms an explosive mixture with air there are problems with storage and transportation before it could be more widely used as a fuel.

Industrial production of hydrogen

- Steam reforming of natural gas (methane)

  The reaction of methane (the main component in natural gas) with steam produces hydrogen as:

$$\underset{\text{Methane}}{CH_4} + H_2O \longrightarrow \underset{\text{Hydrogen}}{3H_2} + CO$$

- Electrolysis of water: by passing an electric current through acidulated water hydrogen and oxygen are produced as:

$$H_2O \longrightarrow H_2 + \tfrac{1}{2}O_2$$

  This process is quite expensive and is usually carried out where cheap electricity is available.

Other industrial uses of hydrogen

- Production of ammonia for fertilisers in the Haber process:

$$N_2 + 3H_2 \xrightarrow{\text{Fe (catalyst)}} 2NH_3$$

- Production of margarine

Hydrogen is used in the food industry to change vegetable oils into margarine. Butter and other animal fats are called saturated fats as they contain single bonds only. Using too much saturated fat such as butter has been linked to heart disease. Margarine or other low fat spreads are termed unsaturated fats as they contain many carbon-carbon double bonds.

To convert vegetable oils from the liquid form to the more solid form requires the addition of hydrogen as some of the double bonds are converted to single bonds.

Sample exam question: 2004 Q6(c)(d)(e) Higher level

(c) Methane is an excellent fuel. Give two properties that account for its usefulness as a fuel. Natural gas is a rich source of methane. Why are mercaptans added to natural gas?

(d) Methane is often found in gas fields which occur in association with crude oil deposits. Crude oil is fractionated in order to obtain more useful products. Outline clearly how the fractionating process is carried out.

(e) Identify two structural features of a hydrocarbon fuel that affect its octane number.

aims To revise the following:
- Preparation and properties of ethene
- Preparation and properties of ethyne
- Preparation and properties of ethanal
- Preparation and properties of ethanoic acid

Mandatory experiment: Preparation and properties of ethene gas

Alkenes can generally be prepared by the dehydration of alcohols i.e. where water is removed.

Ethene, for example, is removed by the dehydration of ethanol as:

$$C_2H_5OH \xrightarrow[\text{Heat}]{Al_2O_3} C_2H_4 + H_2O$$

Aluminium oxide, which is a white solid, acts as a catalyst here.

Elimination reaction

The above reaction is an example of an elimination reaction where a small molecule (in this case water) is removed from a larger molecule leaving a double bond in the larger molecule.

$$
\begin{array}{ccc}
\underset{\text{Ethanol}}{H-\overset{\overset{\displaystyle H}{|}}{\underset{\underset{\displaystyle H}{|}}{C}}-\overset{\overset{\displaystyle H}{|}}{\underset{\underset{\displaystyle H}{|}}{C}}-O-H} & \longrightarrow & \underset{\text{Ethene}}{\overset{\overset{\displaystyle H}{|}}{\underset{\underset{\displaystyle H}{|}}{C}}=\overset{\overset{\displaystyle H}{|}}{\underset{\underset{\displaystyle H}{|}}{C}} + H_2O
\end{array}
$$

There is a structural change here from two tetrahedral carbons in the ethanol molecule to two planar carbons in the ethene molecule.

Procedure

- Place some ethanol in a test tube and then add some glass wool. The glass wool is added after the ethanol to soak up the ethanol.

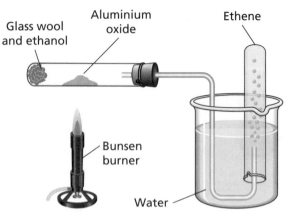

Preparation of ethene

- Set up apparatus as shown in the diagram with about 2 g of aluminium oxide (white) about halfway along the test tube. The aluminium oxide acts as a catalyst during the reaction.

- Heat the aluminium oxide gently. This allows the ethanol to vaporise slowly so that it breaks down slowly into ethene and water.

- Collect at least three test tubes of the gas. The first two test tubes can be discarded as they contain mainly air.

- When finished heating it is important to remove the delivery tube from the water, as a safety precaution, to prevent suck back of water.

Properties of ethene gas

- Colourless with a sweetish smell.

- Not soluble in water but is soluble in non-polar solvents such as cyclohexane. This proves that ethene is non-polar.

- Burns in air with a luminous smoky flame to produce carbon dioxide and water. If some limewater is added to the test tube after burning, the limewater goes milky proving carbon dioxide is present. The reaction is as follows:

$$C_2H_4 \ + \ 3O_2 \ \longrightarrow \ 2CO_2 \ + \ 2H_2O$$
Ethene

Tests for unsaturation

- When bromine water is added to test tube containing ethene there is a colour change from reddish brown to colourless.

$$C_2H_4 \ + \ Br_2 \ \longrightarrow \ C_2H_4Br_2$$
Ethene   Bromine   1,2-dibromoethane

- If a dilute solution of purple potassium manganate (VII) is added to a test tube of ethane, there is a colour change from purple to colourless.

Mandatory experiment: Preparation and properties of ethyne gas

Ethyne belongs to a group of hydrocarbons called the alkynes. These compounds have a triple bond between two carbon atoms and are therefore unsaturated. Ethyne has the molecular formula C_2H_2 and has the following structure:

Ethyne (C_2H_2) $H—C{\equiv}C—H$

Note the triple bond between the carbon atoms.

Preparation of ethyne

Ethyne is prepared by adding water to calcium dicarbide as in the following reaction:

$$CaC_2 \ + \ 2H_2O \ \longrightarrow \ C_2H_2 \ + \ Ca(OH)_2$$

Calcium   Water   Ethyne   Calcium
dicarbide   hydoxide

The apparatus is shown in the diagram below.

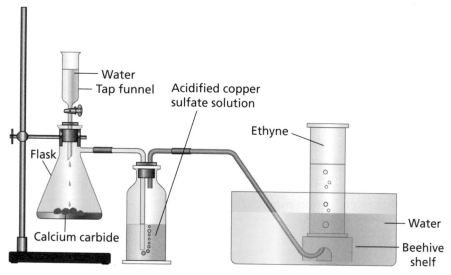

Preparation of ethyne

Purification of the gas: the gas is passed through a solution of acidified copper sulfate to remove the impure gases present.

One impure gas present is hydrogen sulfide (H_2S) and this is caused by the presence of calcium sulfide (CaS) in the calcium dicarbide.

Another impure gas present is phosphine (PH_3) caused by the presence of calcium phosphide in the calcium dicarbide.

Note that it is required that you know both impure gases and their impurities for the Leaving Certificate exam.

Procedure

- Set up the apparatus as shown.
- Allow the water to fall slowly (dropwise) onto the calcium dicarbide as the gas is produced at a very fast rate. Calcium dicarbide is a grey solid.
- The gas is allowed to pass through a solution of acidified copper sulfate to remove the impure gases present and is then collected over water in test tubes.
- The gas can be collected over water like this as it is not soluble in water as it is non-polar and water is polar.
- The first few test tubes of the gas can be discarded as they contain a lot of air. Collect about four test tubes of the gas for tests. Place a cork on each test tube as ethyne is slightly lighter than air.

Properties of ethyne gas

- Burns with a very smoky flame and soot is produced due to the unburned carbon in ethyne.

$$C_2H_2 \; + \; 2\tfrac{1}{2}O_2 \; \longrightarrow \; 2CO_2 \; + \; H_2O$$

- Colourless with a sweetish smell when free of all impurities.
- Not soluble in water but soluble in non-polar solvents.
- Tests for unsaturation can be carried out on ethyne. In the case of ethyne, unsaturation is due to the triple bond between the carbon atoms.

  Test 1: add a solution of acidified potassium manganate(VII) to a test tube of ethyne. Stopper the test tube and shake well. The potassium manganate(VII) solution changes colour from purple to colourless.

  Test 2: add a solution of bromine water to a test tube of ethyne. Again stopper the tube and shake well. The bromine changes colour from reddish-brown to colourless.

Mandatory Experiment: The oxidation of phenylmethanol (benzyl alcohol) to benzoic acid using the oxidising agent potassium manganate (VII) in alkaline conditions.

INTRODUCTION:

- Benzoic acid may be prepared by the oxidation of phenylmethanol using potassium manganate (VII) in the presence of sodium carbonate (alkaline conditions).
- The balanced equation for the reaction is as follows:

$$3C_6 H_5 CH_2 OH + 4 KMnO_4 \rightarrow 3C_6 H_5 COOH + 4 MnO_2 + H_2O + 4 KOH$$

N.B. this reaction will be given in the exams.

- During the reaction there is a structural change from the alcohol to the acid as shown in Fig. 1.

Fig. 1 **Phenylmethanol (benzyl alcohol) is oxidised to benzoic acid by potassium manganate.**

PROCEDURE:

- A solution containing a known mass of phenylmethanol, potassium manganate (VII) and sodium carbonate are heated in a water bath (see step 2 Fig. 2).
- The potassium manganate is present in excess to ensure all the phenylmethanol is oxidised to benzoic acid.
- The sodium carbonate ensures the solution is alkaline as oxidation is faster under alkaline conditions.
- As the reaction proceeds in the conical flask there is a colour change from purple to brown. The reason for this is that the manganese ion is reduced from an oxidation state of $+7$ in $KMnO_4$ where it is purple to an oxidation state of $+4$ in MnO_2 where it is brown.
- A brown precipitate of manganese dioxide is formed in the conical flask and this precipitate is not soluble in water.
- The contents of the conical flask are now cooled under a cold water tap (see step 3 Fig. 2).

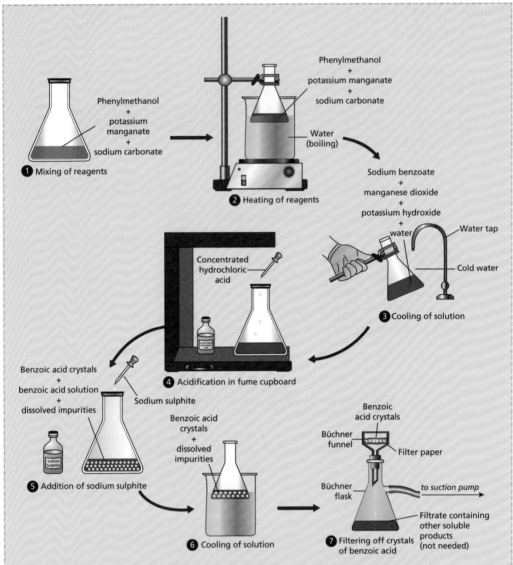

Fig. 2 Summary of steps involved in the oxidation of phenylmethanol (benzyl alcohol) to benzoic acid.

- Following cooling concentrated hydrochloric acid is added dropwise to the conical flask. This should be carried out in a fume cupboard as hydrochloric acid gives off dangerous fumes. To ensure contents of the flask are acidic dip a glass rod into the solution and see does it turn blue litmus red (see step 4 Fig. 2).

- The addition of concentrated hydrochloric acid is added for three reasons:

  (i) to form benzoic acid from sodium benzoate which is an intermediate product in this reaction

(ii) to neutralise any excess sodium carbonate and the basic product potassium hydroxide

(iii) to ensure that the manganese ion is reduced from the brown +4 state to the colourless +2 state.

- Now, using a dropper, sodium sulphite is added until the brown precipitate reacts fully with it. The sodium sulphite is a reducing agent and fully reduces the insoluble solid specks of manganese dioxide that have formed from the +4 state to the colourless +2 state (see step 5 Fig. 2).

- The brown precipitate now disappears and white crystals of benzoic acid are now visible. The solution is now cooled by placing in ice and this further produces benzoic acid crystals as benzoic acid is only slightly soluble in cold water (see step 6 Fig. 2).

- The white crystals of benzoic acid are filtered by pouring the contents of the conical flask through a Büchner funnel (see step 7 Fig. 2).

- The conical flask should be rinsed with the filtrate in the Büchner flask and again passed through the Büchner funnel to ensure all crystals of benzoic have been removed from the conical flask.

- The crystals are washed with ice cold water. This removes any soluble impurities that may be present.

- The damp crystals are allowed to dry overnight and then placed in a dessicator to remove any water still clinging to them.

- The mass of the crystals can be measured and the percentage yield worked out.

aims To revise the following:
- Preparation of soap
- Recrystallisation of benzoic acid
- Measuring the melting point of benzoic acid
- The extraction of clove oil from cloves by steam distillation
- Chromatography and instrumentation

Soap

- A soap is the sodium salt of a long chain organic acid e.g. sodium stearate ($C_{17}H_{35}COONa$).
- A soap is prepared by the alkaline hydrolysis of an animal fat such as lard. This reaction is also called a saponification reaction.
- Animal fats are esters of the alcohol propane-1,2,3-triol (also known as glycerol) and long chain carboxylic acids. This reaction to produce the soap is as follows.

$$
\begin{array}{l}
C_{17}H_{35}-\overset{O}{\underset{\|}{C}}-O-CH_2 \\
C_{17}H_{35}-\overset{O}{\underset{\|}{C}}-O-CH + 3\ NaOH \\
C_{17}H_{35}-\overset{O}{\underset{\|}{C}}-O-CH_2
\end{array}
\longrightarrow
3\ C_{17}H_{35}-\overset{O}{\underset{\|}{C}}-O^-\ Na^+ +
\begin{array}{l}
HO-CH_2 \\
HO-CH \\
HO-CH_2
\end{array}
$$

Glyceryl stearate   Sodium stearate   Glycerol
                              (soap)

Chemical reaction to prepare soap

Animal and vegetable fats

Soaps are produced by the alkaline hydrolysis of animal and vegetable fats.

Animal fats e.g. lard are saturated fats as they consist of single bonds only. Vegetable fats e.g. sunflower oil are unsaturated fats that contain double bonds.

Unsaturated fats like vegetable oil are less damaging to health and these oils can be changed to low fat margarines by addition of hydrogen which converts the oil into a soft solid.

Mandatory experiment: Preparation of a soap

Procedure

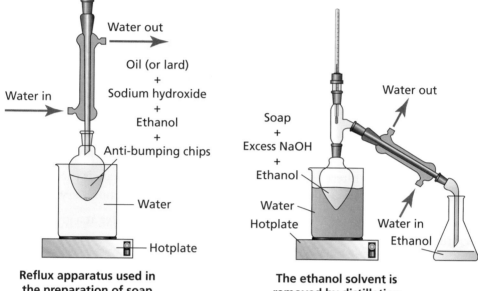

Reflux apparatus used in the preparation of soap

The ethanol solvent is removed by distillation

To prepare the soap by reflux

- Set up the reflux apparatus as shown in the diagram.
- Place a mixture of lard (or vegetable oil), sodium hydroxide and ethanol in the boiling flask. The ethanol is used as a solvent to dissolve the lard as lard is not soluble in water.
- It is important to reflux the mixture as the reaction is slow and refluxing speeds up the reaction. In the reflux process the reaction vapours cool down in the condenser and return to the reaction flask to react again and again. This ensures a more complete reaction and a better yield of product.
- Boil the mixture for 30 minutes. The fat (ester) will now have been converted to a soap. Allow the apparatus to cool.

To isolate the soap

- Rearrange the apparatus for distillation as in the figure. This distillation is carried out at 80 °C to remove the ethanol. Ethanol is removed as it is then easier to separate the soap as the soap dissolves in the ethanol.
- The mixture remaining in the distillation flask is a mixture of soap and excess alkali. The soap must now be separated from the alkali sodium hydroxide.
- The residue from the distillation flask is dissolved in a minimum of hot water in a beaker. A minimum of hot water is used as the soap is soluble in hot water and this would make it harder to isolate the soap.

- A strong solution of brine (sodium chloride) is now added to this solution. The alkali NaOH is soluble in the brine but the soap is not. Therefore the soap forms a precipitate and drops to the bottom of the beaker.
- Filter the soap using a filter funnel. The soap can be washed with brine solution to remove any alkali clinging to it.

Mandatory experiment: To recrystallise benzoic acid and to determine its melting point

Recrystallisation is a technique which is often used to purify organic solids. The basic principle is that:

- the crystalline substance is dissolved in a minimum of hot solvent e.g. water or ethanol
- this hot solution is filtered to remove any impurities. The filtrate is then cooled and on cooling the almost saturated solution solidifies producing purer crystals.

A saturated solution contains as much solid (solute) as it can dissolve at a given temperature.

Procedure

- Place about 5 g of benzoic acid crystals in a clean dry 100 cm³ beaker and add minimum amount of boiling water until the white crystals of benzoic acid have dissolved. It is important to use a minimum of hot water as the crystals will be easier to separate later on when the solution is cooled. Specks of impurity e.g. charcoal will be visible in the water.

To remove the insoluble impurities

- Filter the hot solution through the filter paper in the Buchner funnel. If any crystals form at this stage on the filter paper wash with hot water.

To remove the soluble impurities

- Disconnect the Buchner flask containing the hot filtrate and cool the flask under the cold water tap for a few minutes. Note that white crystals of benzoic acid start to form at this stage.
- Filter off the crystals of benzoic acid from the soluble impurities by pouring the solution from the Buchner flask through a filter funnel with filter paper. The filter paper traps the purer crystals of benzoic acid.

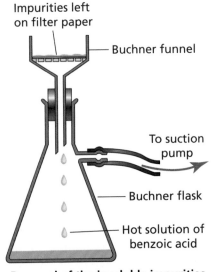

Impurities left on filter paper

Buchner funnel

To suction pump

Buchner flask

Hot solution of benzoic acid

Removal of the insoluble impurities from benzoic acid

Mandatory experiment: To measure the melting point of benzoic acid using an aluminium melting block

Procedure

- Place some crystals of benzoic acid on the surface of a clean aluminium block into which a thermometer has been placed as in the diagram. Note the thermometer must be capable of reading at least 150 °C as the melting point of benzoic is about 120 °C.
- Place the block on a hotplate. Turn on the hotplate and observe the crystals as they melt. Note the reading on the thermometer.
- Allow the block to cool and repeat for two more readings of the temperature. Take an average.

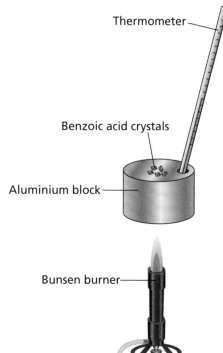

Thermometer

Benzoic acid crystals

Aluminium block

Bunsen burner

To measure the melting point of benzoic acid

Melting point and purity

It is important to note that the melting point of solids is an indicator of purity.

- If the crystals of benzoic acid are pure they should melt at the given melting point for benzoic acid.
- If the crystals are impure, they will melt at a lower temperature and over a range of temperatures.
- The formula for benzoic acid is C_6H_5COOH.

Use of benzoic acid

Benzoic acid is used as a food preservative.

Mandatory experiment: The extraction of clove oil from cloves by steam distillation

Theory of steam distillation

- Steam distillation can be used to extract oils from plant material. In this experiment the oil eugenol is extracted from cloves. It is important to note that when a mixture of water and an insoluble liquid like oil are heated they boil at a temperature which is less than the boiling point of either liquid.
- Steam distillation involves passing a current of steam over the plant material. The steam causes the oil to vapourise and the mixture of oil and steam is passed through a condenser to form a liquid. The liquid collected is a cloudy white emulsion of clove oil and water.
- Steam distillation rather than ordinary distillation is used as ordinary distillation requires too high a temperature and this would destroy the cloves causing them to char and decompose.

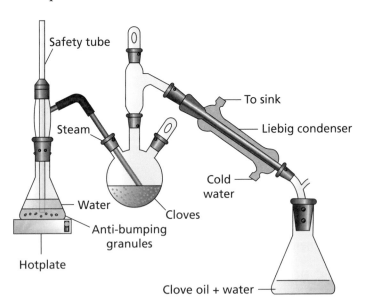

Procedure

- Boil the water in the steam generator. A safety tube is used to allow the steam to escape. It is important to put this tube under the level of liquid in the reaction vessel otherwise steam will escape without reaching the cloves.
- The heat is regulated so that a constant current of steam passes into the flask containing the cloves. Whole cloves are used rather than ground cloves as they contain more oil.
- The distillate comes across as an emulsion i.e. the oil is dispersed through the water as tiny droplets.

Solvent extraction of clove oil

- Liquid–liquid extraction (also called solvent extraction) is a method whereby two immiscible liquids e.g. clove oil and water are separated using a solvent e.g. cyclohexane in which one of the liquids in the mixture is more soluble.
- In this extraction the two immiscible liquids are clove oil and water and the solvent is cyclohexane. Clove oil is very soluble in cyclohexane as both are non-polar. Water however is not soluble in cyclohexane as water is polar.

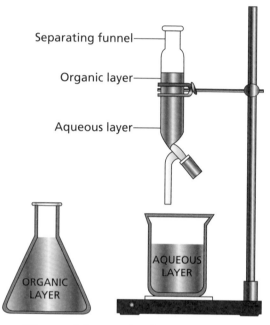

Separating funnel

Organic layer

Aqueous layer

ORGANIC LAYER

AQUEOUS LAYER

When cyclohexane is added to the clove oil emulsion, the organic layer floats on the aqueous layer.

The separating funnel must be held firmly when in use and the tap opened after shaking to release the pressure of vaporised liquid.

Procedure

- The oil from the emulsion will be extracted three times during the experiment using 10 cm³ portions of cyclohexane.
- Set up a separating funnel containing about 50 cm³ of clove oil emulsion. Add 10 cm³ of cyclohexane to the funnel.
- Two layers are now visible i.e. cyclohexane floats on the water as it is not soluble in water and it is less dense than water.
- Now the two layers are thoroughly mixed. This is achieved by placing a stopper on the funnel, then inverting the funnel and shaking the funnel. It is important to open the tap of the funnel while shaking it to release pressure of vapourised liquid.

- Now place the separating funnel in a retort stand again. Open the tap and release the lower aqueous layer as it contains no clove oil.
- Now add 10 cm^3 of cyclohexane and repeat the mixing and separating procedure. Again release the aqueous layer.
- Repeat mixing and separating for a third addition of 10 cm^3 cyclohexane.

The structure of eugenol is required at higher level only.

Eugenol is the main constituent of oil of cloves.

Safety aspects of this preparation

- It is important to use gloves and safety spectacles during this experiment as there is a danger of scalding.
- When sufficient distillate has been collected, it is important to disconnect the apparatus at the steam condenser to avoid suck-back.
- A safety tube is used to allow the steam to escape.

Uses of clove oil

Clove oil is used in flavourings, perfumes and in medicine.

Chromatography and instrumentation in organic chemistry

What is the basic principle of chromatography?

Chromatography is a separation of a mixture of components based on different interactions between a mobile phase and a stationary phase. The stationary phase can be paper or solid while the mobile phase can be liquid or gas.

Mandatory experiment: To separate a mixture of coloured substances e.g. a mixture of indicators using paper chromatography

Procedure

- Apply the mixture using a dropper onto a sheet of chromatography paper or filter paper. The drops of the mixture should be placed about 2 cm from the bottom of the sheet as shown in the diagram.
- The sheet should be placed in a gas jar as shown, with the spot of mixture just above the level of the solvent e.g. water and ethanol.
- The solvent moves up the paper as each of the components of the mixture dissolves to a different extent in the solvent.

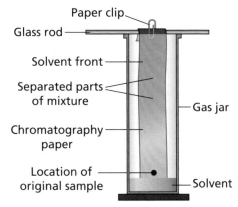

Paper clip

Glass rod

Solvent front

Separated parts of mixture

Gas jar

Chromatography paper

Location of original sample

Solvent

Paper chromatography may be used to separate the different colours in ink

- The components of the mixture will be separated according to their solubility i.e. the least soluble components in the solvent will come out of the solution first and be deposited onto the paper. The more soluble components will stay in the solution longer and be deposited higher up.
- Result: the different components of the mixture are separated according to their solubility as shown in the diagram.

Gas chromatography

As in other chromatography techniques, the underlying principle of this technique is that different components of a mixture are separated by their different interactions with the mobile phase and the stationary phase.

Gas chromatography is more advanced than paper chromatography and is particularly useful for the separation of components in a volatile (low boiling point) mixture e.g. blood alcohol analysis.

Gas chromatography uses a gas e.g. nitrogen as the mobile phase.

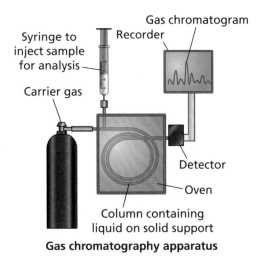

Gas chromatogram

Recorder

Syringe to inject sample for analysis

Carrier gas

Detector

Oven

Column containing liquid on solid support

Gas chromatography apparatus

The stationary phase is a high boiling point (non-volatile) liquid spread on solid particles (e.g. silica gel) packed into a long coiled tube called a column as in diagram.

The different processes occurring here are as follows:

1. **Injection and transport:** the sample mixture is injected into the instrument by a syringe and is carried into the column by a flow of gas e.g. nitrogen gas.

2. **Separation and detection:** separation occurs in the column containing the liquid on a solid support which is contained in a temperature-controlled oven. The components of the mixture are separated due to the fact that some components are more soluble in the liquid than others.

Therefore the components of the mixture are separated as they flow out of the column into a detector that records a signal.

This detector plots a chart called a gas chromatogram where each component of the mixture is shown as a peak.

Uses of gas chromatography

- To measure the level of alcohol in blood.
- Drug tests for athletes.

High performance liquid chromatography

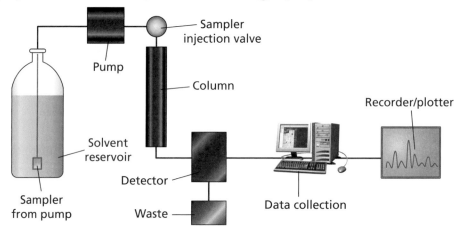

High performance liquid chromatography

- In this type of chromatography the mobile phase is a liquid solvent into which the mixture to be separated is added.
- This solvent is then pumped under pressure into a column which contains the stationary phase which is a finely divided solid. Again separation is achieved as some components of the mixture are less soluble in the solvent than others.
- Separation in high performance liquid chromatography is more efficient than in the gas chromatography and therefore the column need not be as long.

The sample is analysed by studying the gas chromatogram formed.

Uses

- Testing for drugs.
- Testing for growth promoters in meat.

Mass spectrometer

The basic principle of the process is that the components of a mixture are separated and identified according to their masses in a magnetic field.

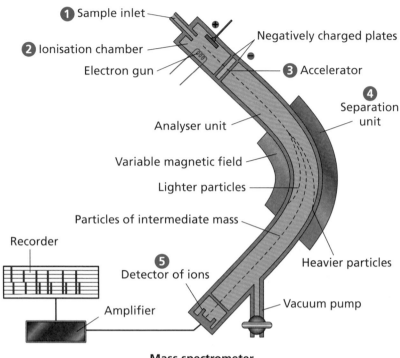

Mass spectrometer

Stages in the mass spectrometer

1. **Vaporisation of sample**

   A small amount of the sample of the gas or liquid is introduced into the sample inlet. As there is a good vacuum inside the liquid sample will turn to a gas.

2. **Ionisation of sample producing positive ions**

   The heated filament gives off electrons, which knock electrons out of the atoms or molecules of the sample creating positive ions.

3. **Acceleration**

   The positive ions from the ionization chamber are attracted by negative plates, which cause them to reach high speeds.

4. **Separation of isotopes**

   The positive ions are forced to move in a curved path by the magnetic field. The lighter particles are deflected more than the heavier ones and therefore the particles are separated according to their masses.

5. **Detection**

   The ions are electronically detected and the signal is magnified and recorded producing a mass spectrum.

Uses of the mass spectrometer

- Measurement of relative atomic mass.
- Finding number and abundance of isotopes of an element.

- Analysing organic pollutants in water.
- Analysing waste gases from dumps.

Gas chromatography is often used in conjunction with mass spectrometry where the separated components that emerge from the gas chromatography apparatus are passed into the mass spectrometer which enables each compound to be analysed and identified. This combination technique is called GC-MC analysis.

HL Infrared absorption spectrometry

Infrared light has a longer wavelength than visible light and is given off by hot objects.

The principle of this type of spectrometry is that molecules of a substance absorb infrared light of different wavelengths. The combination of wavelengths absorbed by a substance helps to identify the substance.

In infrared absorption spectrometry a sample of the substance under investigation is placed between a source of infrared light and a detector. The detector analyses the infrared light absorbed by the sample and a recorder draws a graph. Each compound has a unique infrared spectrum and therefore it can be identified when compared with a database of compounds.

Uses of infrared absorption spectrometry

- In drug tests.
- Can be used to identify plastics.

Ultraviolet absorption spectrometry

The main principle of ultraviolet absorption spectrometry is that the absorption of ultraviolet light by a substance is directly proportional to the concentration of that substance.

In this type of spectrometry a solution of the substance under investigation is placed between a source of ultraviolet light and a detector. The detector analyses the light after it passes through the sample and the absorption spectrum obtained shows what wavelengths of light have been absorbed. Usually maximum absorption occurs at a particular wavelength and this can be used not only to identify the compound but to determine its concentration as well.

Use of ultraviolet absorption spectrometry

- In drug tests e.g. to test for certain organic compounds.

18 Stoichiometry

Percentage composition

Sample problem: 2003 Q4(g) Higher level

Find the percentage by mass of nitrogen in ammonium nitrate (NH_4NO_3).   (6 marks)

Solution

$$\text{percentage mass of nitrogen} = \frac{\text{total mass of nitrogen}}{\text{total mass of compound}} \times 100$$

Mass of the nitrogen atom = 14. There are two atoms of nitrogen in this compound so the total mass of nitrogen = 28

Mass of ammonium nitrate (NH_4NO_3) = $2(14) + 4(1) + 3(16) = 80$ (3 marks)

$$\text{Percentage mass of nitrogen} = \frac{28}{80} \times 100$$
$$= 35\%$$ (3 marks)

Empirical formula and molecular formula

The empirical formula of a compound gives the simplest ratio of the atoms of each element present in a molecule of a compound.

The molecular formula of a compound gives the actual ratio of the atoms of each element present in a molecule of a compound.

To calculate the empirical formula of a compound given its composition by mass

Sample exam question: 2005 Q4(h) Higher level

When 3.175 g of copper reacts with chlorine gas 6.725 g of copper chloride is formed. Find the empirical formula of the chloride.   (6 marks)

Solution

$$\text{mass of chlorine} = 6.725 - 3.175 = 3.55 \text{ g}$$

To establish the simplest ratio divide the mass of each element by its atomic mass:

Copper	Chlorine
$\dfrac{3.175}{63.5}$	$\dfrac{3.55}{35.5}$

Ratio   0.05   :   0.1   (3 marks)

To establish the simplest ratio divide across by $0.05 = 1 : 2$ (3 marks)

Therefore empirical formula of copper chloride is: $CuCl_2$

To calculate the empirical and molecular formula of a compound given its percentage composition

Sample problem

An organic compound is composed of 54.5% carbon, 9.1% hydrogen and 36.4% oxygen. Find its empirical formula.

If the relative molecular mass of the compound is 88 find its molecular formula. Suggest a possible name for the compound and draw its structural formula.

Solution

Element	Percentage	Percentage divided by relative atomic mass	Simplest ratio (divide by 2.27)
Carbon	54.5	$54.5 \div 12 = 4.54$	2
Hydrogen	9.1	$9.1 \div 1 = 9.1$	4
Oxygen	36.4	$36.4 \div 16 = 2.27$	1

Empirical formula $= C_2H_4O$

To establish the molecular formula

$$(C_2H_4O) \times n = 88$$
$$[2(12) + 4(1) + 16] \times n = 88$$
$$44n = 88$$
$$n = 2$$

Therefore the molecular formula $= (C_2H_4O) \times 2 = C_4H_8O_2$

Name for compound

As the organic compound has two oxygen atoms it could be a carboxylic acid or an ester. The carboxylic group is COOH.

Therefore the acid is C_3H_7COOH which is butanoic acid.

key
definition

Structural formula is the spatial arrangement of atoms in one molecule of a compound.

The structure of butanoic acid is given here.

$$
\begin{array}{ccccc}
 & H & H & H & \\
 & | & | & | & \\
H\!-\!C\!-\!C\!-\!C\!-\!C\!=\!O \\
 & | & | & | & | \\
 & H & H & H & O\!-\!H
\end{array}
$$

Butanoic acid

Balancing chemical equations

When writing a chemical equation you must do the following.

- First write the equation in words.
- Write down the correct formula for each compound.
- Balance the equation by putting numbers in front only.

Example

Ethane burns in oxygen to form carbon dioxide and water.

  (i) Write the chemical equation.

  (ii) Calculate the mass of water produced when 3 g of ethane is completely burned in oxygen.

 (iii) Find the number of molecules of carbon dioxide formed.

Solution

Write the correct formula for each compound:

$$C_2H_6 \ + \ O_2 \ \longrightarrow \ CO_2 \ + \ H_2O$$

Balance the equation by putting numbers in front only. In this combustion equation balance in the order carbon, hydrogen and then balance the oxygens as they are uncombined. The final balanced equation is:

  (i) $C_2H_6 \ + \ 3\frac{1}{2}O_2 \ \longrightarrow \ 2CO_2 \ + \ 3H_2O$

  (ii) finding mass of water produced

       3 g of ethane used. Change to moles.

          1 mole ethane $= 30$ g

          $3 \div 30 = 0.1$ moles

       0.1 moles of produces 0.3 moles of water

       therefore mass of water $= 0.3 \times 18 = 5.4$ g of water

(iii) finding the number of molecules of carbon dioxide formed in this reaction.

0.1 moles of ethane produces 0.2 moles carbon dioxide

1 mole $= 6 \times 10^{23}$ molecules

0.2 moles $= 0.2 \times 6 \times 10^{23} = 1.2 \times 10^{23}$ molecules

Exam type questions: More difficult equation problem

Chlorine gas was prepared by reacting 3.95 g of potassium manganate(VII) with excess concentrated hydrochloric acid.

The equation for the reaction is:

$$2KMnO_4 \quad + \quad 16HCl \quad \longrightarrow \quad 2KCl \quad + \quad 2MnCl_2 \quad + \quad 8H_2O \quad + \quad 5Cl_2$$

(i) How many moles of hydrogen chloride were used?

(ii) What was the total mass of chlorides produced?

(iii) How many water molecules were produced?

(iv) What volume of chlorine at s.t.p. was obtained? How many atoms of chlorine are in this volume?

(1 mole at s.t.p. $= 22.4$ litres $= 6 \times 10^{23}$ molecules)

Solution

Good idea to divide equation across by 2 giving:

$$KMnO_4 \quad + \quad 8HCl \quad \quad KCl \quad + \quad MnCl_2 \quad + \quad 4H_2O \quad + \quad 2.5Cl_2$$

$\quad$ 1 mole $\qquad$ 8 moles $\quad$ 1 mole $\quad$ 1 mole $\qquad$ 4 moles $\quad$ 2.5 moles

(i) How many moles of HCl?

First find moles of $KMnO_4$

$$Number\ of\ moles = \frac{actual\ mass}{molar\ mass} = \frac{3.95}{158} = 0.025\ moles$$

0.025 moles of $KMnO_4$ reacts with 8 (0.025) moles of HCl

$\Rightarrow 0.2$ moles of HCl were used.

(ii) What is the total mass of chlorides produced?

Looking for moles and mass of KCl and $MnCl_2$

Moles of KCl $= 0.025$ moles

$\qquad = 0.025 \times 74.5 = 1.8625\ g$

Moles of $MnCl_2 = 0.025$ moles

$\qquad = 0.025 \times 126 = 3.15\ g$

$\Rightarrow$ total mass of chlorides $= 3.15 + 1.8625 = 5.0125\ g$

(iii) How many water molecules were produced?

moles of water $= 4\ (0.025) = 0.1$ moles

but 1 mole $= 6 \times 10^{23}$ molecules

0.1 moles $= 6 \times 10^{22}$ molecules

(iv) What volume of chlorine was produced?

moles of Cl_2 = 0.025 × 2.5 = 0.0625 moles

1 mole = 22.4 litres at s.t.p.

0.0625 moles = 0.0625 × 22.4 = 1.4 litres

How many atoms of chlorine?

1 mole = 6 × 10^{23} molecules

0.0625 moles = 0.0625 × 6 × 10^{23} molecules

= 3.75 × 10^{22} molecules

but 1 molecule of Cl_2 = 2 atoms

⟹ 3.75 × 2 × 10^{22} atoms = 7.5 × 10^{22} atoms.

Calculations based on limiting reactants

A reactant is said to be limiting if it is not present in excess in a reaction.

The limiting reactant determines the amount of product that can be formed in a reaction as the following examples will show.

2007 Q2(d) Higher level

A sample of ethanoic acid was prepared by the oxidation of ethanol. The reaction is represented by the following equation:

$$3C_2H_5OH + 2Cr_2O_7^{2-} + 16H^+ \longrightarrow 3CH_3COOH + 4Cr^{3+} + 11H_2O$$

Show clearly that ethanol is the limiting reagent when 8 cm³ of ethanol (density = 0.8 g/cm³) was added to 29.8 g of sodium dichromate ($Na_2Cr_2O_7 \cdot 2H_2O$). There was excess sulfuric acid present. (12 marks)

Solution

- Convert each reactant to moles
- Moles of dichromate = $\dfrac{\text{actual mass}}{\text{molar mass}}$

$$= \frac{29.8}{298} = 0.1 \text{ moles} \qquad \text{(3 marks)}$$

- Moles of ethanol
  first convert to mass

$$\text{density} = \frac{\text{mass}}{\text{volume}}$$

$$0.8 = \frac{\text{mass}}{8}$$

$$\text{mass} = 8 \times 0.8 = 6.4 \text{ g} \quad \text{(3 marks)}$$

$$\text{moles of ethanol} \frac{6.4}{46} = 0.139 \text{ moles} \qquad \text{(3 marks)}$$

- Comparing molar quantities to determine the limiting reactant (which is not in excess).

From the balanced equation:

3 moles ethanol require 2 moles of dichromate

1 mole ethanol requires $\dfrac{2}{3}$ mole of dichromate

0.139 moles ethanol requires $\dfrac{2}{3}$ (0.139) = 0.093 moles of dichromate

0.1 moles of dichromate is present in this reaction and therefore the dichromate is in excess and ethanol is the limiting reagent.   (3 marks)

It is important to note that in the above reaction the ethanol dictates how much ethanoic acid can be formed as it is the limiting reagent. Therefore the maximum amount of ethanoic acid that can be formed in the above reaction is 0.139 moles and this is called the theoretical yield.

Percentage yield

key
definition

The percentage yield $= \dfrac{\text{actual yield}}{\text{theoretical yield}} \times 100$

Sample problem on percentage yield: Preparation of ethanal

Ethanal was prepared by the oxidation of ethanol using the following quantities: 14.9 g of sodium dichromate ($Na_2Cr_2O_7 \cdot 2H_2O$) dissolved in 10 cm³ of water and 9.2 g of ethanol was added.

The reaction may be represented as:

$$3C_2H_5OH + Cr_2O_7^{2-} + 8H^+ \longrightarrow 3CH_3CHO + 2Cr^{3+} + 7H_2O$$

Calculate

   (i) Number of moles of ethanol.

  (ii) Number of moles of sodium dichromate used.

 (iii) Explain why sodium dichromate is the limiting reagent.

 (iv) If 2.9 g of ethanal was obtained what is the percentage yield of ethanal?

Solution

   (i)   mass of ethanol = 9.2 g

      no. of moles $= \dfrac{9.2}{46} = 0.2$ moles of ethanol

(ii) moles of dichromate $= \dfrac{\text{actual mass}}{\text{molar mass}}$

$$= \dfrac{14.9}{298} = 0.05 \text{ moles dichromate}$$

(iii) In the balanced equation the ratio of moles reacting are:

$$3C_2H_5OH \ + \ Cr_2O_7^{2-} \longrightarrow 3CH_3CHO$$

3 moles of ethanol require 1 mole of dichromate.
0.2 moles of ethanol requires $0.2 \div 3 = 0.0667$ moles of dichromate

However, only 0.05 moles of dichromate are being used.
Therefore sodium dichromate is the limiting reagent i.e. the reagent that is not in excess.

(iv) To calculate the percentage yield
0.05 moles of dichromate produces 3 (0.05) ethanal $= 0.15$ moles of ethanal
This is the theoretical yield.
convert to mass in grams

$$0.15 \text{ moles of ethanal} = 0.15 \times 44 = 6.6 \text{ g}$$

$$\text{percentage yield} = \dfrac{\text{actual yield}}{\text{theoretical yield}} \times 100$$

$$= \dfrac{2.9}{6.6} \times 100 = 43.9\%$$

Rate of reaction

Rate of reaction is defined as a change in concentration in unit time of any one reactant or product.

$$\text{Rate} = \frac{\text{change in concentration}}{\text{time}}$$

Example: decomposition of hydrogen peroxide:

$$H_2O_2 \xrightarrow{\ MnO_2\,(\text{catalyst})\ } H_2O + \tfrac{1}{2}O_2$$

If initial concentration of hydrogen peroxide is 1 mole/litre and after five seconds it has decreased to 0.25 moles/litre then

$$\text{Reaction rate} = \frac{1 - 0.25}{5} = 0.15 \text{ moles/litre/sec}$$

HL Average and instantaneous rates of reaction

- Average rate $= \dfrac{\text{change in reactant (or product)}}{\text{time}}$
- Instantaneous rate of reaction is the rate of reaction at any particular moment in time. This can be measured from the slope of the graph as in the following example.

Mandatory experiment: To monitor the rate of production of oxygen from hydrogen peroxide using manganese dioxide as a catalyst

Hydrogen peroxide decomposes into water and oxygen readily in the presence of manganese dioxide (MnO_2) catalyst. The reaction is:

$$H_2O_2 \xrightarrow{MnO_2} H_2O + \tfrac{1}{2}O_2$$

Hydrogen
peroxide

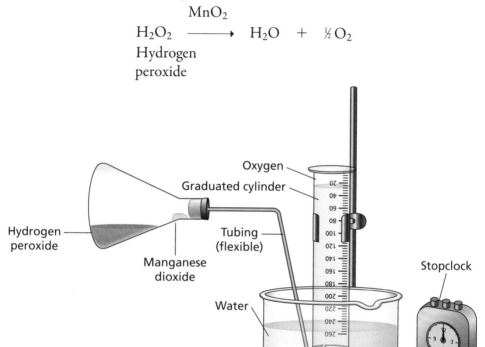

Apparatus to measure the rate of production of oxygen gas

Procedure

It is important before starting this experiment that one person takes charge of reading the volume of oxygen and another person reads the time using a stop watch.

- Set up the apparatus as shown in the diagram.
- Place 50 cm³ of hydrogen peroxide initially in the conical flask.
- Fill the graduated cylinder with water and invert in a water bath as shown.
- Place a small amount of manganese dioxide into the neck of the conical flask as shown.
- Allow the manganese dioxide to fall into the hydrogen peroxide and immediately start the stop watch. It is imperative that the timing starts immediately when the catalyst comes in contact with the peroxide solution.
- At half minute intervals record the volume of oxygen released in the graduated cylinder.
- Continue measuring the gas until the reaction is over i.e. when there is no further release of oxygen gas.
- Draw a graph of volume of oxygen released against time.

HL Sample exam question: 2008 Q3(d)(e) Higher level

(d) The table shows the volumes of gas (at room temperature and pressure) produced at intervals over 12 minutes.

Time (mins)	0	1	2	3	5	7	9	11	12
Volume (cm³)	0	20	36	50.5	65.5	73	76.5	78	78

Plot a graph of volume released versus time.

Explain why the graph is steepest in the beginning.   **(15 marks)**

(e) Use your graph to:

    (i) determine the instantaneous rate of gas production at five minutes

    (ii) calculate the total mass of gas produced in this experiment.   **(12 marks)**
      (molar volume at room temperature and pressure = 24 litres)

Solution

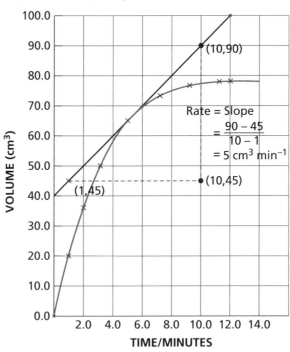

QUESTION 3(d): Graph

Rate = Slope
$$= \frac{90 - 45}{10 - 1}$$
$$= 5 \text{ cm}^3 \text{ min}^{-1}$$

(10,90)

(10,45)

(1,45)

VOLUME (cm³)

TIME/MINUTES

(d) plot:

- Axes accurately labelled with numbers   (3 marks)
- Axes with correctly labelled units   (3 marks)
- Eight points correctly plotted   (3 marks)
- Curve accurately drawn from origin   (3 marks)

Explain: the graph is steepest in the beginning as there is the greatest concentration of hydrogen peroxide which gives the greatest rate.   (3 marks)

(Note the word 'amount' is not acceptable for 'concentration')

(e) (i) instantaneous rate = slope of graph = $\dfrac{90 - 45}{10 - 1}$

$\qquad\qquad\qquad = 5\ cm^3 min^{-1}$ $\qquad$ (6 marks)

(Note any answer in the range 4.0 – 6.0 was accepted)

Also note that if the average rate had been asked after 5 minutes, the calculation would be $65.5 \div 5 = 13.1\ cm^3 min^{-1}$

(ii) Total volume of gas released = 78 cm^3

convert to litres: $78 \div 1000 = 0.078$ litres

convert to moles: $0.078 \div 24 = 0.00325$ moles $\qquad$ (3 marks)

convert to grams: mole of $O_2 = 32$ g

0.00325 moles $= 32 \times 0.00325 = 0.104$ g $\qquad$ (3 marks)

Factors affecting reaction rate

1. Nature of reactants

In general ionic reactions are fast while covalent reactions are slow. In ionic reactions when the ions collide they react e.g. in the reaction between silver nitrate ($AgNO_3$) and sodium chloride the white precipitate of silver chloride is formed immediately. The reason for this is that the when the ions collide they react as:

$$Ag^+ + Cl^- \longrightarrow AgCl\ \text{(silver chloride)}$$

Covalent reactions are slower than ionic as covalent bonds must be broken first, for example in the combustion of methane to form carbon dioxide and water.

$$CH_4 + 2O_2 \longrightarrow CO_2 + 2H_2O$$

In this reaction the C—H bonds in methane and O=O bonds in oxygen must be broken first. Then the C=O bonds in carbon dioxide and the O—H bonds in water must be formed before the reaction is complete.

2. Particle size

In a reaction involving a solid and a liquid, the more finely divided the solid is, the faster the reaction. For example, a lump of marble (calcium carbonate) takes a lot longer to react with dilute HCl than if marble chips were used, or indeed powdered calcium carbonate. The reason for this is that there is a greater surface area for the reaction to occur and therefore more effective collisions can occur, forming a product.

Dust explosions

Dust explosions provide an everyday example of how particle size affects the rate of a chemical reaction.

In flour mills, grain silos and coal mines very small particles in an enclosed space can give rise to a very vigorous reaction, leading to an explosion.

There are four main ingredients necessary for dust explosions:

- very fine particles of dust which are combustible
- a source of ignition e.g. a light or spark

- oxygen to support the combustion
- an enclosed space.

3. Concentration of reactants

An increase in the concentration of one of the reactants usually increases the reaction rate. For example:

$$Mg \ + \ 2HCl \ \longrightarrow \ MgCl_2 \ + \ H_2$$

Magnesium   Hydrochloric   Magnesium   Hydrogen

acid   chloride   gas

The more concentrated the acid, the more rapidly the hydrogen is liberated. The reason for this is that the greater the concentration of reactant particles, the greater the chance of effective collisions occurring and forming a product.

4. Temperature

All reactions are faster at higher temperatures. An increase of 10 K generally doubles the reaction rate. The reason for this is that the molecules get greater kinetic energy and reach the activation energy faster and therefore more effective collisions occur, forming a product.

5. Catalyst

A catalyst is a substance which alters the rate of a chemical reaction without being used up itself. For example, hydrogen and oxygen hardly react at all at room temperature but in the presence of platinum wire the reaction occurs rapidly. The reason for this is that the catalyst lowers the activation energy for the reaction by making it easier for the reaction to occur and form products.

6. Pressure

This only applies to gaseous reactions. Increasing pressure of a gas increases its concentration and puts the molecules closer together.

This again increases the number of effective collisions forming a product and therefore increases the rate of the reaction.

HL Sample exam question: 2003 Q7(a) Higher level

Calcium carbonate (marble chips) reacts with hydrochloric acid according to the following equation:

$$CaCO_3 \ + \ 2HCl \ \longrightarrow \ CaCl_2 \ + \ CO_2 \ + \ H_2O$$

Using simple experiments involving marble chips ($CaCO_3$) and hydrochloric acid describe how to show the effects of (i) particle size (ii) concentration on the rate of a chemical reaction. **(18 marks)**

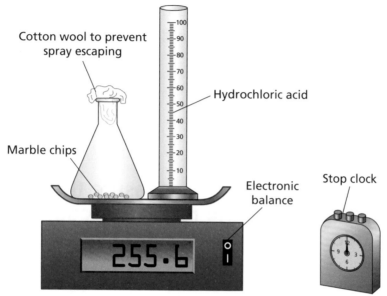

Apparatus to investigate the effect of particle size and concentration on the rate of reaction

For both experiments the apparatus is shown in the diagram.

Solution

(i) To show the effect of particle size

Procedure

- The conical flask contains large marble chips initially and the graduated cylinder contains dilute hydrochloric acid. A cotton wool plug is used to prevent any loss of spray during the experiment. (3 marks)
- The total mass of the apparatus is read from the balance at the start. The dilute hydrochloric acid is added to the marble chips and a stop clock is started. (3 marks)
- The mass is recorded every 30 seconds for about ten minutes. The loss in mass is due to the release of carbon dioxide gas.
- Record the time when there is no further loss of mass. (3 marks)
- Repeat the experiment but this time use small granules of marble. All other conditions are kept constant for a fair test e.g. concentration of the dilute hydrochloric acid. Again record the time when there is no further loss in mass.

Result and conclusion

Using the smaller particles it will be noted that the loss in mass occurs much faster and the reaction is completed in a shorter time. The reason for this is that the smaller particle size creates a greater surface area for the reaction. This results in more effective collisions forming a product.

(ii) To show the effect of concentration

- The above experiment can be repeated using equal masses of equal sized particles. (3 marks)
- Add equal volumes of different concentration of hydrochloric acid. (3 marks)
- Again note the time when there is no further loss in mass. (3 marks)

The time recorded will be less than that for the diluted acid showing that increasing the concentration increases the rate. The reason for this is that with increased concentration there is a greater chance of effective collisions forming a product.

Mandatory experiment: To measure the effect of concentration on the rate of reaction using sodium thiosulfate solution and hydrochloric acid

In this experiment the reaction of sodium thiosulfate and hydrochloric acid is used. This reaction produces a yellow precipitate of sulfur according to the following equation:

$$2HCl + Na_2S_2O_3 \longrightarrow 2NaCl + S + SO_2 + H_2O$$

Hydrochloric acid · Sodium thiosulfate · Sulfur precipitate

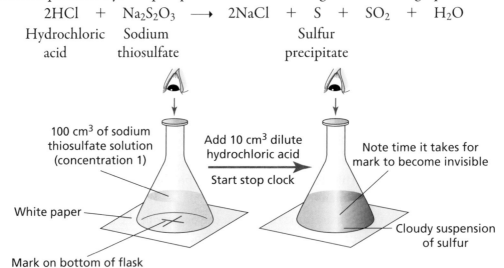

100 cm³ of sodium thiosulfate solution (concentration 1)

Add 10 cm³ dilute hydrochloric acid
Start stop clock

Note time it takes for mark to become invisible

White paper

Cloudy suspension of sulfur

Mark on bottom of flask

Apparatus

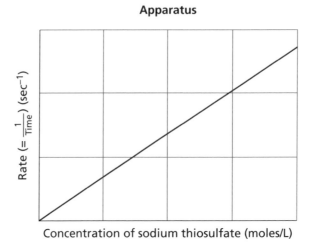

Rate (= $\frac{1}{Time}$) (sec^{-1})

Concentration of sodium thiosulfate (moles/L)

Graph of results

Procedure

- Using a graduated cylinder place 100 cm³ of 0.1 M solution of sodium thiosulfate into a conical flask. Place the conical flask on a white sheet of paper as shown on which an X has been made.
- Using another graduated cylinder add 10 cm³ of hydrochloric acid solution to the flask. Immediately start a stop clock.
- Time how long it takes for the X to disappear due to the cloudiness of the yellow precipitate of sulfur produced. Record the time.
- Repeat steps 1, 2 and 3 but this time use a weaker 80% solution of sodium thiosulfate. This 80% solution is obtained by mixing 80 cm³ of the 0.1 M thiosulfate solution with 20 cm³ of deionised water in a graduated cylinder. The concentration of this solution is therefore 80% of 0.1 M = 0.08 M. The time involved here will be longer as the concentration is less. Record the time.
- Repeat steps 1, 2 and 3 but this time use a weaker 60% solution of sodium thiosulfate. This 60% solution is obtained by mixing 60 cm³ of the 0.1 M thiosulfate solution with 40 cm³ of deionised water in a graduated cylinder. The concentration of this solution is therefore 60% of 0.1 M = 0.06 M. Record the time.
- Repeat the same procedure for 40% (0.04 M) and 20% (0.02 M) solutions of sodium thiosulfate. The time recorded will be progressively longer.
- Construct a table of results and draw a graph of rate $= \frac{1}{time}$ against concentration and the result is a straight line through the origin proving that rate of reaction is directly proportional to concentration. It is important to note here that rate is proportional to $\frac{1}{time}$ as the smaller the time, the faster the rate and vice-versa.

Mandatory experiment: To measure the effect of temperature on the rate of reaction

In this experiment the reaction of sodium thiosulfate and hydrochloric acid is used. This reaction produces a yellow precipitate of sulfur according to the following equation:

$$2HCl \ + \ Na_2S_2O_3 \ \longrightarrow \ 2NaCl \ + \ S \ + \ SO_2 \ + \ H_2O$$

Hydrochloric   Sodium   Sulfur

acid   thiosulfate   precipitate

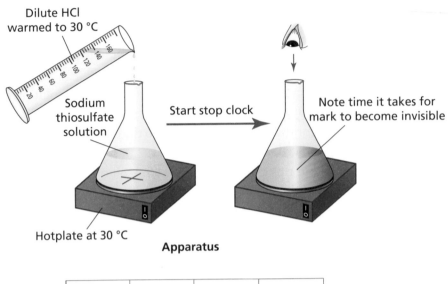

Apparatus

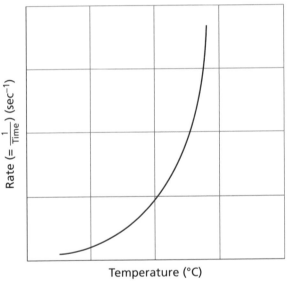

Graph of results

Procedure

- Using a graduated cylinder place 100 cm³ of 0.05 M solution of sodium thiosulfate into a conical flask. Place the conical flask on a white sheet of paper as shown on which an X has been made.
- Using another graduated cylinder add 10 cm³ of hydrochloric acid solution to the flask. Immediately start a stop clock.
- Time how long it takes for the X to disappear due to the cloudiness of the yellow precipitate of sulfur produced. Record the time. Record the temperature of the solution e.g. 15 °C.
- Wash out the conical flask and again add 100 cm³ of 0.05 M solution of sodium thiosulfate into a conical flask . Warm the flask on a hotplate as shown in the

diagram to a temperature of 20 °C. Add the HCl solution and measure the time taken for the X to disappear. Record the time.

- Repeat previous step using different temperatures of 30 °C, 40 °C, 50 °C and 60 °C.
- Again draw a graph of temperature against rate ($\frac{1}{time}$).
- It is important to note here that rate is not directly proportional to $\frac{1}{time}$ as increases in temperature cause much larger increases in reaction rate as shown in graph.

Catalysts

A catalyst is a substance which alters the rate of a chemical reaction without being used up in the reaction.

Types of catalysts

Homogeneous catalysis is where the catalyst and reactants are in the same phase.

An example of homogeneous catalysis is reaction between ethanol and ethanoic acid to form an ester. This reaction is catalysed by the presence of dilute sulfuric acid.
The reactants and catalysts here are all liquids and the reaction is:

$$H_2SO_4 \text{ (l)}$$

$$\begin{array}{ccccccc} C_2H_5OH & + & CH_3COOH & \longrightarrow & CH_3COOC_2H_5 & + & H_2O \\ \text{(l)} & & \text{(l)} & & \text{(l)} & & \text{(l)} \\ \text{Ethanol} & & \text{Ethanoic acid} & & \text{Ethyl ethanoate} & & \text{Water} \end{array}$$

Heterogeneous catalysis is where the catalyst and reactants are in different phases.

An example of heterogeneous catalysis is in the synthesis of ammonia by the Haber process. In this reaction a solid iron catalyst is used but the reactants are gases.

$$Fe(s)$$

$$\begin{array}{ccccc} N_2 & + & 3H_2 & \longrightarrow & 2NH_3 \text{ (ammonia)} \\ \text{(g)} & & \text{(g)} & & \text{(g)} \end{array}$$

key definition

Autocatalysis occurs when one of the products formed catalyses the reaction.

An example of autocatalysis occurs in the redox reaction of potassium manganate(VII) ($KMnO_4$) and iron(II) sulfate. The ionic reaction is:

$$MnO_4^- + 5Fe^{2+} + 8H^+ \longrightarrow Mn^{2+} + 5Fe^{3+} + 4H_2O$$

The Mn^{2+} ions produced catalyse the reaction and the change of colour from purple to colourless is more rapid as the reaction proceeds (see redox titrations).

HL Theories of catalysis

Surface adsorption theory

The surface adsorption theory refers to heterogeneous catalysis (two distinct phases e.g. gas reactants and solid catalyst).

Ethene and hydrogen adsorb onto nickel surface forming temporary bonds

Reaction occurs: $C_2H_4 + H_2 \longrightarrow C_2H_6$

- The main principle of this theory is that the catalyst provides a surface on which the reactants can react with each other.
- Ethene gas (C_2H_4), for example, reacts with hydrogen (H_2) in the presence of a nickel catalyst.
- Both reactant gases adsorb onto the Ni surface and are held by weak bonds. Therefore the reactants come into more close contact with each other and react to form ethane gas (C_2H_6).

Product ethane desorbs from surface leaving surface free to adsorb other reactants

Surface adsorption theory

- When the product ethane gas is formed it escapes (desorbs) from the surface allowing more reactants to take its place.
- The more finely divided the catalyst, the greater the reaction rate. The reason for this is that more reaction sites become available and the easier it is for the reactants e.g. ethene and hydrogen to react.

Intermediate formation theory

- The main principle of this theory is that a catalyst works by forming an intermediate compound which is unstable and breaks down to form products regenerating the catalyst.
- In an uncatalysed reaction reactant A reacts slowly with reactant B as follows:

$$A + B \longrightarrow AB \quad \text{slow reaction}$$

- However, if a catalyst C is introduced two fast reactions occur.

Reactant A reacts quickly with the catalyst to form an intermediate compound AC as follows:

$$A + C \longrightarrow AC \quad \text{fast reaction}$$
$$\text{intermediate compound}$$

- Then the intermediate compound AC reacts quickly with the other reactant B to produce the product AB and the catalyst is released to be used again.

$$AC + B \longrightarrow AB + C \quad \text{fast reaction}$$

Thus a slow reaction has in effect been replaced by two fast reactions.

Specified demonstration: Example of intermediate formation theory

- The oxidation of potassium sodium tartrate by hydrogen peroxide is an example of this theory. The potassium sodium tartrate is dissolved in hot water and some crystals of pink cobalt chloride are added as a catalyst.
- The starting solution is pink due to the catalyst.
- Then some hydrogen peroxide solution is added and the colour changes to green. This green colour is due to the formation of an intermediate compound and there is a vigorous release of carbon dioxide and steam.
- The pink colour then returns at the end showing that the catalyst is not used up and the products are formed.

Catalytic converters

- Catalytic converters are fitted to a car exhaust as in the diagram to reduce emissions of the pollutant gases carbon monoxide (CO), nitrogen monoxide (NO) and nitrogen dioxide (NO_2).

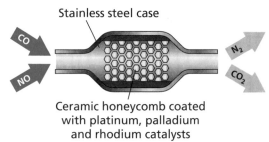

Stainless steel case

Ceramic honeycomb coated with platinum, palladium and rhodium catalysts

A typical catalytic converter

- These three gases are poisonous gases. The oxides of nitrogen also contribute to acid rain.
- The converter contains the catalysts platinum (Pt), palladium (Pd) and rhodium (Rh).

These metals speed up the following reaction:

$$\overset{\text{Pt/Pd/Rh}}{2CO + 2NO \longrightarrow 2CO_2 + N_2}$$

Carbon   Nitrogen   Carbon   Nitrogen
monoxide monoxide   dioxide

- Therefore this reaction removes the harmful gases carbon monoxide and nitrogen monoxide replacing them with the gases nitrogen and carbon dioxide.

It is important to note that lead in petrol acts as a catalytic poison to the catalysts in the catalytic converter. The lead atoms bond to the platinum/rhodium surface and thereby block the active sites thus preventing the catalysts from working properly. This is why unleaded petrol is used in cars fitted with catalytic converters.

HL Collision theory and activation energy

exam focus

The main points of the collision theory are as follows:

- for a reaction to occur the colliding particles must react with each other
- in order for the collisions to be effective i.e. to form a product, the colliding particles must have reached a certain minimum energy.

key definition

Activation energy (E_A) is the minimum energy colliding particles must have to form a product.

Energy profile diagrams

- These diagrams show the activation energy as an energy barrier that must be overcome for the reactants to form products.
- They also show whether a reaction is going to be exothermic or endothermic.
- If the energy of the products is greater than the energy of the reactants then the reaction is endothermic. Therefore, heat has been removed from the surroundings and the heat of reaction (ΔH) is positive.

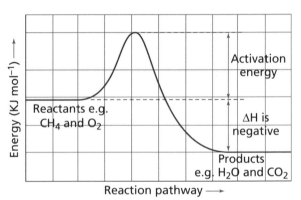

Energy profile diagram for an exothermic reaction

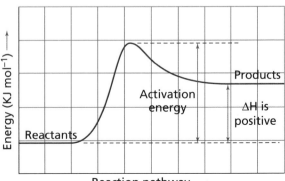

Energy profile diagram for an endothermic reaction

- If the energy of the products is smaller than the energy of the reactants then the reaction is exothermic. Therefore, heat has been released into the surroundings and the heat of reaction (ΔH) is negative.
- In a catalysed reaction, the catalyst lowers the activation energy but the overall heat of reaction does not change.

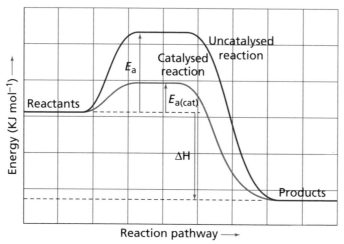

A catalyst lowers the activation energy for a reaction

Specified demonstration: The oxidation of methanol to methanal using a hot platinum wire

The reaction for the oxidation of methanol to methanal in the presence of the catalyst hot platinum wire is:

$$2CH_3OH \ + \ O_2 \ \xrightarrow{\text{hot Pt}} \ 2HCHO \ + \ 2H_2O$$

Methanol   Methanal

This is an example of heterogeneous catalysis where the catalyst (solid) and the reactants (both gases) are in different phases.

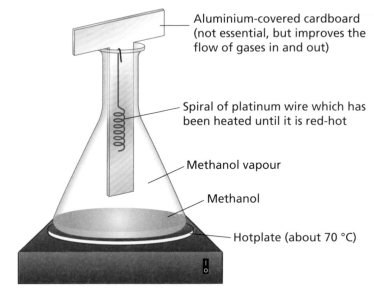

Aluminium-covered cardboard (not essential, but improves the flow of gases in and out)

Spiral of platinum wire which has been heated until it is red-hot

Methanol vapour

Methanol

Hotplate (about 70 °C)

The platinum goes through a cycle of glowing red hot and then cooling

The oxidation of methanol using a platinum catalyst

Procedure

- It is important to wear safety goggles for this experiment and it should be carried out in a fume cupboard as methanol is toxic.
- Warm 25 cm^3 of methanol in a conical flask placed on a hotplate.
- Heat a spiral of platinum wire to red heat in a Bunsen flame well away from the methanol.
- Quickly hang the spiral into the flask on one side of the cardboard insert. The cardboard insert wrapped in kitchen foil improves the flow of gases in and out.
- The spiral which will have cooled during the transfer to below red hot will begin to glow again.
- There may be number of mild explosions and the spiral will be seen to go through a cycle of glowing red hot and then cooling.

20 Chemical Equilibrium

Reversible reactions and dynamic equilibrium

Consider the reversible reaction:

$$H_2 + I_2 \rightleftharpoons 2HI$$

Some reactions never go to completion where the reactants are completely changed into products. Instead the reaction is reversible where there is a forward and a reverse reaction going on as in the above reaction:

the forward reaction is: $H_2 + I_2 \longrightarrow 2HI$

and the reverse reaction is: $2HI \longrightarrow H_2 + I_2$

Equilibrium constants

There is a mathematical relationship between the concentrations of reactants and products in an equilibrium mixture called the equilibrium constant (K_c). Look at the general reaction.

$$mA + nB \rightleftharpoons pC + qD$$

At equilibrium in this reaction m moles of A reacts with n moles of B to produce p moles of C and q moles of D.

Therefore the equilibrium constant is given by:

$$K_c = \frac{[C]^p[D]^q}{[A]^m[B]^n}$$

In the reaction: $H_2 + I_2 \rightleftharpoons 2HI$

The equilibrium constant is written as:

$$K_c = \frac{[HI]^2}{[H_2][I_2]}$$

HL It is important to note that:
- the value of the K_c is temperature dependent
- the units depend on the relative number of moles on each side of the equation for the reaction. Units are not required for the Leaving Certificate exam.

Example 1: Calculation of equilibrium constants 2002 Q10(c) Higher level (18 marks)

When 30 g of ethanoic acid and 23 g of ethanol were placed in a conical flask and a few drops of concentrated sulfuric acid were added, an equilibrium was set up with the formation of ethyl ethanoate and water. The equilibrium is represented by the following equation:

$$CH_3COOH + C_2H_5OH \rightleftharpoons CH_3COOC_2H_5 + H_2O$$

When the equilibrium mixture was analysed it was found to contain 10 g of ethanoic acid.
(i) Write the equilibrium constant for the reaction.   (6 marks)
(ii) Calculate the value of the equilibrium constant K_c.   (12 marks)

Solution

(i) $K_c = \dfrac{[CH_3COOC_2H_5][H_2O]}{[CH_3COOH][C_2H_5OH]}$ (6 marks)

(ii) Initial and equilibrium concentrations must be converted to moles.

Initial moles of ethanoic acid: $30 \div 60 = 0.5$ moles
Initial moles of ethanol: $23 \div 46 = 0.5$ moles
Equilibrium moles of ethanoic acid: $10 \div 60 = 0.167$ moles
Therefore change in concentration of ethanoic acid $= 0.5 - 0.167 = 0.333$ moles

	CH$_3$COOH	C$_2$H$_5$OH	CH$_3$COOC$_2$H$_5$	H$_2$O
Initial	0.5 moles	0.5 moles	0 moles	0 moles (3 marks)
Change	0.5−0.333	0.5−0.333	0.333	0.333 (3 marks)
Equilibrium	0.167	0.167	0.333	0.333 (3 marks)

$$K_c = \frac{[CH_3COOC_2H_5][H_2O]}{[CH_3COOH][C_2H_5OH]}$$

$$= \frac{(0.333)(0.333)}{(0.167)(0.167)} = 4 \quad (12 \text{ marks})$$

Note that in this example there was no need to mention the volume as the volumes would cancel in the equilibrium expression.

Example 2: Volume type calculation 2004 Q9(e) Higher level

Consider the following reversible reaction:

$$N_2 + 3H_2 \rightleftharpoons 2NH_3$$

In an experiment 6.0 moles of nitrogen gas and 18.0 moles of hydrogen gas were mixed and allowed to come to equilibrium in a sealed five litre container. It was found that there were six moles of ammonia in the equilibrium mixture.

Write down the equilibrium constant expression for the reaction and calculate the value of the equilibrium constant K_c for the reaction. (18 marks)

Solution

$$K_c = \frac{[NH_3]^2}{[N_2][H_2]^3} \quad (6 \text{ marks})$$

It is important in these problems to be conscious of the ratios of reactants and products.

$$N_2 + 3H_2 \rightleftharpoons 2NH_3$$

1 mole   3 moles   2 moles

Ratio: 1 : 3 : 2

Therefore to produce six moles of ammonia at equilibrium the reacting ratios would apply:

3 moles N_2 : 9 moles H_2 : 6 moles NH_3

	N_2	H_2	NH_3
Initial	6 moles	18 moles	0 moles (3 marks)
Change	6 − 3 moles	18 − 9 moles	6 moles (3 marks)
Equilibrium (moles/litre)	$\frac{3}{5} = 0.6$	$\frac{9}{5} = 1.8$	$\frac{6}{5} = 1.2$ (3 marks)

$$K_c = \frac{[NH_3]^2}{[N_2][H_2]^3} = \frac{(1.2)^2}{(0.6)(1.8)^3} = 0.4 \quad (3 \text{ marks})$$

Example 3: Calculation where the equilibrium constant is given

A gaseous mixture of hydrogen, iodine and hydrogen iodide form an equilibrium mixture according to the following equation:

$$H_2 + I_2 \rightleftharpoons 2HI$$

(i) Write the equilibrium constant expression for the system.   (6 marks)

(ii) The value of the equilibrium constant, K_c, for the reaction is 50 at 721 K. If two moles of hydrogen iodide gas were introduced into a sealed vessel at this temperature calculate the number of moles of hydrogen iodide gas present when equilibrium is reached.   (12 marks)

Solution:

(i) $K_c = \dfrac{[HI]^2}{[H_2][I_2]}$ (6 marks)

(ii) $H_2 + I_2$ $2HI$

ratios   1   :   1   :   2

Let x moles of hydrogen and x moles of nitrogen be formed at equilibrium. The ratios in terms of x would be:

x moles N_2 : x moles I_2 : 2x moles HI

	H_2	I_2	HI
Initial	0 moles	0 moles	2 moles
Change	X moles	X moles	$-2x$ moles
Equilibrium	X moles	X moles	$2 - 2x$ moles

$$K_c = \frac{[HI]^2}{[H_2][I_2]} = \frac{(2 - 2x)^2}{(x)(x)} = 50$$

The easiest way to solve this equation is to get the square root of both sides:

$$\frac{2 - 2x}{x} = 7.07$$

$$2 - 2x = 7.07x$$

$$9.07x = 2$$

$$x = 0.22 \text{ moles}$$

Amount of hydrogen iodide left $= 2 - 2(0.22)$

$$= 1.56 \text{ moles}\quad \text{(12 marks)}$$

Le Chatelier's principle

key definition

When a stress is applied to a system at equilibrium a change occurs to oppose the stress and equilibrium is restored.

Examples of stresses that can be applied to a system are changes in (i) temperature (ii) concentration and (iii) pressure.

Changes in pressure would apply to gaseous reactions only.

An example of a chemical equilibrium situation is the conversion of hydrogen and nitrogen to ammonia as in the following reaction:

$$N_2 \ + \ 3H_2 \ \overset{Iron(Fe)}{\rightleftharpoons} \ 2NH_3 \quad \Delta H = -98 \ kJ/mole$$

Iron acts as a catalyst in this reaction.

Let us examine what effect the following changes would have on the above reaction.

1. Change in concentration

- If more nitrogen or hydrogen is added, the forward reaction (left to right) occurs, which uses up these reactants and increases the yield of ammonia.
- If more ammonia is added (or hydrogen or nitrogen is removed), the backward reaction (right to left) takes place and the concentration of ammonia is reduced. The concentration of hydrogen and nitrogen is increased.

2. Change in pressure

If the pressure is increased, the reaction will go in the direction that will reduce the pressure. There are four molecules on the left side of the reaction and only two on the right and therefore the forward reaction will occur as this reduces the pressure by decreasing the volume. This will result in an increase in the concentration of ammonia.

3. Change in temperature

The reaction is exothermic going forward (left to right) and endothermic going backward.

- If the temperature is increased, the system opposes this change by absorbing the heat and therefore the backward endothermic reaction occurs reducing the concentration of ammonia.
- If the temperature is reduced, the forward exothermic reaction occurs to release heat to oppose this stress. Therefore in lowering the temperature the production of ammonia is favoured.

4. Adding a catalyst

Adding a catalyst lowers the activation energy for a reaction and therefore the equilibrium is reached faster. However, it does not alter the concentration of the products at equilibrium.

Industrial applications of Le Chatelier's principle

1. The manufacture of ammonia by the Haber process

Ammonia is used in the manufacture of fertilisers and the Haber process used is named after the scientist Fritz Haber who used Le Chatelier's principle to devise the best conditions for the highest yield of ammonia.

$$N_2 \ + \ 3H_2 \ \underset{\text{Iron(Fe)}}{\rightleftharpoons} \ 2\,NH_3, \Delta H = -98 \text{ kJ/mole}$$

Pressure

- As described above high pressures drive the equilibrium from left to right and suits the production of ammonia.
- In the industrial production of ammonia increased pressures are used but the pressure is not allowed to go too high as with increased pressure there is increased cost and safety issues (thicker pipes etc.) so a compromise of about 200 atmospheres is reached.

Temperature

- As described above low temperatures cause a greater yield of ammonia as the forward exothermic reaction is favoured.
- In industry, in practice, a low temperature is not used as this slows down the reaction. Therefore a compromise temperature of about $450\,°C$ is used so that the reaction is not uneconomically slow.

2. The manufacture of sulfuric acid by the contact process

In the manufacture of sulfuric acid, sulfur trioxide (SO_3) is produced from sulfur dioxide using oxygen as:

$$2SO_2 \ + \ O_2 \ \underset{V_2O_5}{\rightleftharpoons} \ 2SO_3 \qquad \Delta H = -98 \ Kj/mole$$

The catalyst used here is vanadium pentoxide.

Pressure

- If the pressure is increased the reaction will go the side with the lower number of molecules. There are three molecules on the left side of the reaction and only two on the right and therefore the forward reaction will occur. This increases the concentration of sulfur trioxide.
- In practice, however, in industry, increasing the pressure increases the cost as there are safety issues and therefore a compromise pressure of just above atmospheric is used.

Temperature

- If the temperature is reduced the forward exothermic reaction occurs to release heat to oppose this stress. Therefore in lowering the temperature the production of sulfur trioxide is favoured.
- However, as in the case of ammonia, decreasing the temperature too much would slow down the reaction making it uneconomical. Therefore a compromise temperature is reached in practice so that the reaction can proceed at a reasonable rate.

Mandatory experiment: Simple experiment to illustrate Le Chatelier's principle

Reaction: A solution of iron(III) chloride and potassium thiocyanate

This reaction can be represented by the following equation:

$$FeCl_3 \ + \ CNS^- \ \rightleftharpoons \ Fe(CNS)^{2+} \ + \ 3Cl^-$$

$$\text{Yellow} \qquad\qquad\qquad\qquad \text{Red}$$

Procedure

1. Mix together equal (5 cm^3) solutions of iron(III) chloride and potassium thiocyanate in a beaker. The solution is now red.
2. In a fume cupboard add some concentrated hydrochloric acid. The addition of acid adds Cl^- ions and therefore the equilibrium goes from right to left to absorb these ions. Therefore the colour changes from red to yellow.
3. Now add some iron(III) chloride and the reaction goes from left to right and the red colour is restored again.

21 Oxidation and Reduction

aims To revise the following:

- Oxidation and reduction in terms of electron transfer
- Oxidising and reducing agents
- Redox reactions of group VII elements
- The electrochemical series
- Electrolysis
- Oxidation and reduction in terms of oxidation numbers
- Balancing redox equations using oxidation numbers

Oxidation and reduction in terms of electron transfer

key definition

Oxidation is the loss of electrons by an atom or ion. Reduction is the gain of electrons by an atom or ion.

Memory aid: OIL RIG (oxidation is loss, reduction is gain).

Example 1

Magnesium reacts with oxygen in the air forming magnesium oxides and loses its shine. The reaction of magnesium and oxygen is shown:

$$Mg \quad + \quad \tfrac{1}{2}O_2 \quad \longrightarrow \quad MgO$$

Magnesium   Oxygen   Magnesium oxide

- In this reaction the magnesium atom gives two electrons to an oxygen atom. Therefore magnesium is oxidised as it loses electrons and oxygen is reduced as it gains electrons.
- The magnesium atom becomes the magnesium ion (Mg^{2+}) and the oxygen atom becomes the oxygen ion (O^{2-}).
- It is important to note that whenever oxidation occurs reduction must also occur. Reactions where both oxidation and reduction both occur are called redox reactions.

Everyday example of oxidation and reduction

Rusting of iron is an everyday example of oxidation and reduction. The iron reacts with oxygen in the air according to the equation:

$$2Fe \quad + \quad 1\tfrac{1}{2}O_2 \quad \longrightarrow \quad Fe_2O_3 \text{ (Iron(III) oxide)}$$

Rust

- The iron atoms (Fe) lose three electrons each to become Fe^{3+} ions and are therefore oxidised.
- The oxygen atoms (O) gain two electrons each to become O^{2-} ions and are therefore reduced.

Oxidising and reducing agents

key
definition

An oxidising agent is a substance which causes another substance to be oxidised.
A reducing agent is a substance that causes another substance to be reduced.

Example 2

In the reaction of sodium metal with chlorine, sodium chloride is formed.

$$Na \quad + \quad \tfrac{1}{2}Cl_2 \quad \longrightarrow \quad NaCl$$

- The sodium atom donates one electron to the chlorine atom. Therefore sodium is oxidised as it loses an electron and chlorine is reduced as it gains an electron.
- The sodium atom is the reducing agent as it reduces chlorine. Note that the reducing agent is itself oxidised.
- The chlorine atom is the oxidising agent and is itself reduced.

Everyday examples of oxidising and reducing agents

- Bleaches can act as either oxidising or reducing agents.
  (i) Household bleach contains sodium hypochlorite (NaOCl) which produces the ion OCl^- which is an oxidising agent. Sodium hypochlorite is also used in the treatment of swimming pool water as it kills harmful microorganisms by oxidising them.
  (ii) Bleach containing the reducing agent sulfur dioxide is used to bleach paper a yellow colour.

Mandatory experiment: Redox reactions of the halogens (Group VII)

(a) To show that the halogens are oxidising agents

- The halogens (chlorine, bromine, iodine, etc.) gain one electron when they react and are reduced.
- The halogens, therefore, act as oxidising agents.

To show the oxidation of sulfite (SO_3^{2-}) ions to sulfate (SO_4^{2-}) ions by a halogen e.g. chlorine.

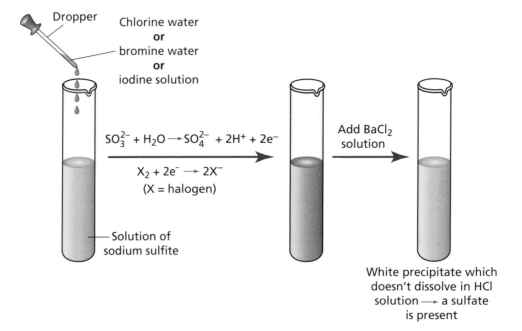

Dropper

Chlorine water
or
bromine water
or
iodine solution

$SO_3^{2-} + H_2O \longrightarrow SO_4^{2-} + 2H^+ + 2e^-$

$X_2 + 2e^- \longrightarrow 2X^-$
(X = halogen)

Solution of sodium sulfite

Add BaCl$_2$ solution

White precipitate which doesn't dissolve in HCl solution → a sulfate is present

Procedure

- Add a solution of chlorine water to a solution of sodium sulfite in a test tube as shown. The following half reactions occur where the sulfite ion is oxidised and chlorine is reduced.
  (i) SO_3^{2-} + H_2O $\longrightarrow$ SO_4^{2-} + $2H^+$ + $2e^-$
      Sulfite ion   Sulfate ion

  Here the sulfite ion loses two electrons to become the sulfate ion.
  (ii) Cl_2 + $2e^-$ $\longrightarrow$ $2Cl^-$
  Chlorine gains two electrons and is reduced. Therefore chorine is the oxidising agent.
- To prove that the sulfate ion has been produced add barium chloride solution and a few drops of dilute hydrochloric acid.
- A white precipitate is formed which is insoluble in the hydrochloric acid. This indicates the presence of sulfate ions. If they were soluble in the hydrochloric acid they would be sulfite ions.

(b) To show the oxidation of Fe^{2+} ions to Fe^{3+} ions by the halogen chlorine

Procedure

- Add a solution of chlorine water to an acidified solution of iron(II) sulfate. Dilute sulfuric acid is added to prevent the Fe^{2+} ions being oxidised to Fe^{3+} by oxygen in the air.
- Now add some sodium hydroxide solution to the mixture.
- A greenish-brown precipitate should form showing the presence of Fe^{3+} ions therefore iron(II) ions have been oxidised to iron(III) ions according to the equation.

$$Fe^{2+} \longrightarrow Fe^{3+} + 2e^-$$

- The chlorine gains two electrons and is therefore the oxidising agent.

$$Cl_2 + 2e^- \longrightarrow 2Cl^-$$

(c) To compare the oxidising ability of the halogens

The oxidising ability of halogens decrease down the group as the electronegativity decreases down the group.

Chlorine for example has a greater oxidising ability than either bromine or iodine and this can be shown as follows.

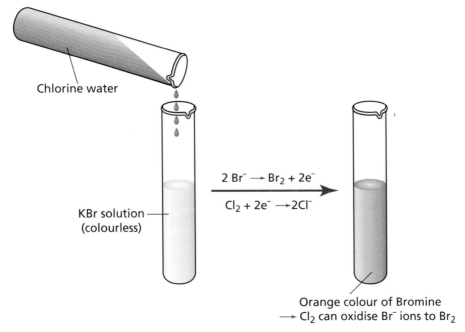

Chlorine water

KBr solution
(colourless)

$$2\,Br^- \longrightarrow Br_2 + 2e^-$$
$$Cl_2 + 2e^- \longrightarrow 2Cl^-$$

Orange colour of Bromine
→ Cl_2 can oxidise Br^- ions to Br_2

To show chlorine is a stronger oxidising agent than bromine

Procedure

- Add 2 cm³ of a chlorine water solution to an equal volume of potassium bromide (KBr) solution. The following reaction occurs.

$$Cl_2 + 2Br^- \longrightarrow Br_2 + 2Cl^-$$

The orange colour of bromine appears which proves that the bromide ion has lost electrons to chlorine and become bromine atoms. Therefore bromine has been oxidised by chlorine.

- Now add 2 cm^3 of a chlorine water solution to an equal volume of potassium iodide (KI) solution. The following reaction occurs.

$$Cl_2 + 2I^- \longrightarrow I_2 + 2Cl^-$$

The reddish-brown colour of iodine appears which proves that the iodide ion has lost electrons to chlorine and become iodine atoms. Therefore iodine has been oxidised by chlorine.

- Finally add 2 cm^3 of a bromine water solution to an equal volume of potassium iodide (KI) solution. The following reaction occurs.

$$Br_2 + 2I^- \longrightarrow I_2 + 2Br^-$$

The reddish-brown colour of iodine appears which proves that the iodide ion has lost electrons to bromine and become iodine atoms. Therefore iodine has lost electrons to bromine and has therefore been oxidised by bromine.

Conclusion

The above experiments prove that the oxidising ability of the three halogens examined is in the order $Cl > Br > I$.

Electrochemical series of metals

key definition

The electrochemical series of metals is a series of metal listed in order of their ability to lose electrons (electrode potential).

Electrochemical series

Memory aid (top to bottom): **Poor Chaotic Student Makes A Zillion Improvements Learning His Chemistry Success Guide!**

- Elements at the top of the list, e.g. potassium and calcium, have a great tendency to lose electrons and be oxidised. Therefore they are very reactive.
- A metal will displace a metal below it in the series from a solution of its salt e.g. if a piece of magnesium ribbon is placed in a solution of copper sulfate it will become coated with copper. The reaction is

$$Mg + CuSO_4 \longrightarrow MgSO_4 + Cu$$

- *Hydrogen is not a metal but is placed in series to show where it lies in terms of reactivity.

Potassium	K	Very reactive
Calcium	Ca	
Sodium	Na	
Magnesium	Mg	
Aluminium	Al	
Zinc	Zn	
Iron	Fe	
Lead	Pb	
*Hydrogen	H	
Copper	Cu	
Silver	Ag	
Gold	Au	Least reactive

Mandatory experiment: Displacement reactions of metals

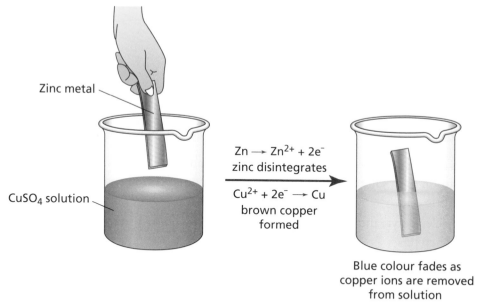

Zinc metal

$Zn \longrightarrow Zn^{2+} + 2e^-$
zinc disintegrates

$Cu^{2+} + 2e^- \longrightarrow Cu$
brown copper formed

CuSO₄ solution

Blue colour fades as copper ions are removed from solution

To show that zinc displaces copper from copper sulfate

Procedure

- Half fill a test tube with copper(II) sulfate solution.
- Place a zinc rod dipping in the tube.
- It will be noted that:
  (i) the zinc becomes coated with copper
  (ii) the blue colour of the copper(II) sulfate solution starts to fade.
      The reaction occurring is:

$$Zn \ + \ CuSO_4 \ \longrightarrow \ ZnSO_4 \ + \ Cu$$

In this reaction Zn loses two electrons to copper.

$$Zn \ + \ Cu^{2+} \ \longrightarrow \ Zn^{2+} \ + \ Cu$$

Therefore zinc is oxidised and copper is reduced. Thus this reaction shows zinc has a greater tendency to lose electrons than copper.

- Now place a piece of magnesium metal in some copper(II) sulfate solution. Note again that the magnesium becomes coated with metal and the blue colour of the solution fades.

The reaction which occurs is:

$$Mg \ + \ CuSO_4 \ \longrightarrow \ MgSO_4 \ + \ Cu$$

In this reaction magnesium loses two electrons to copper.

$$Mg \ + \ Cu^{2+} \ \longrightarrow \ Mg^{2+} \ + \ Cu$$

Application of displacement reactions

Scrap iron can be used to extract copper from a solution of copper salts as shown.

$$Fe \ + \ Cu^{2+} \ \longrightarrow \ Cu \ + \ Fe^{2+}$$

Electrolysis

key
definition

Electrolysis is the use of an electric current to bring about a chemical reaction.

- An electrolyte is a substance that can conduct an electric current when melted or in solution e.g. a solution of molten (melted) sodium chloride or a dilute solution of sulfuric acid.
- The electrolyte must be melted or in solution to allow the free movement of ions through it.

Examples of electrolysis

Electrolysis of copper(II) sulfate solution with active copper electrodes

Procedure

- Set up the apparatus as shown with two copper rods dipping into copper(II) sulfate solution. One copper rod is the cathode or negative electrode and the other copper rod is the anode or positive electrode.

  Memory aid to remember polarity of cathode and anode: CATNAP = cathode negative anode positive.
- The electrodes here are called active electrodes as they react with the electrolyte.

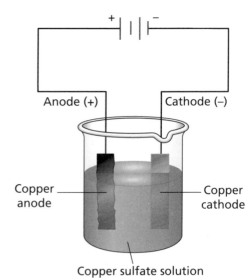

Anode (+)   Cathode (–)

Copper anode   Copper cathode

Copper sulfate solution

The electrolysis of copper sulfate using copper electrodes

- Cathode reaction (negative electrode)

  It is important to note that reduction occurs at the cathode as it is a negative electrode and donates electrons.

  Memory aid: Red Cat (reduction at cathode).

Copper(II) ions from the solution receive two electrons at the cathode and solid copper plates out on the cathode.

$$Cu^{2+}_{(aq)} + 2e^- \longrightarrow Cu_{(s)}$$

- Anode reaction (positive electrode):

$$Cu_{(s)} \longrightarrow Cu^{2+}_{(aq)} + 2e^-$$

Here copper atoms at the anode lose two electrons and enter the solution as copper ion. Oxidation occurs at the anode.

- The overall result of this electrolysis is the copper anode slowly dissolves in the solution and pure copper is deposited on the cathode. This electrolysis is used in industry to purify copper.

Electrolysis of acidulated water using inert platinum electrodes

Procedure

- In this electrolysis inert platinum electrodes are used. The word inert signifies that the electrodes are not reactive and do not get involved in the electrolysis.
- A Hoffmann voltameter apparatus is used to pass an electric current through water to which some dilute sulfuric acid has been added.
- Hydrogen gas is produced at the cathode (negative electrode) and oxygen gas is produced at the anode (positive electrode).
- Cathode reaction (reduction)

$$2H^+ + 2e^- \longrightarrow H_2$$

Hydrogen ions in the solution receive two electrons and produce hydrogen gas at the cathode.

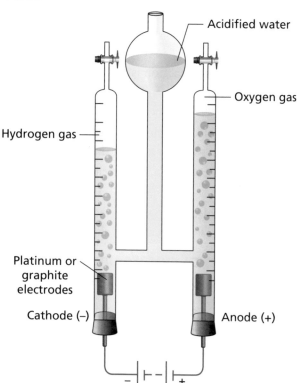

The electrolysis of acidulated water using inert platinum electrodes

1. Anode reaction (oxidation)

$$H_2O \longrightarrow \tfrac{1}{2}O_2 + 2H^+ + 2e^-$$

Water molecules break down at the anode, producing oxygen gas.

The overall reaction is the breakdown of water into hydrogen and oxygen.

$$H_2O \longrightarrow \tfrac{1}{2}O_2 + H_2$$

It is important to note that there is twice as much hydrogen produced as oxygen and this proves that the correct formula for water is H_2O.

(HL) Electrolysis of aqueous sodium sulfate using inert platinum electrodes and universal indicator

Procedure

- A few drops of universal indicator are added to the sodium sulfate solution and an electric current is then passed through the solution. Universal indicator is red in acidic solution, blue in basic solution and green when neutral.

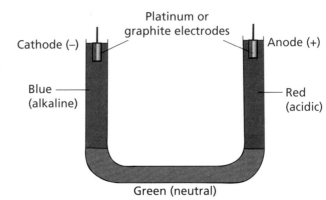

Cathode (–) Platinum or graphite electrodes Anode (+)

Blue (alkaline) Red (acidic)

Green (neutral)

The electrolysis of sodium sulfate using inert electrodes

- The cathode reaction is reduction.

$$2H_2O + 2e^- \longrightarrow H_2 + 2OH^-$$

Water molecules gain two electrons here producing negative hydroxyl ions which makes the solution around the cathode alkaline and the colour is blue.

- The anode reaction is oxidation.

$$H_2O \longrightarrow \tfrac{1}{2}O_2 + 2H^+ + 2e^-$$

Water molecules lose two electrons here producing positive hydrogen ions which makes the solution around the anode acidic and the colour is red.

Electrolysis of potassium iodide using inert electrodes and phenolphthalein indicator

Procedure

- A few drops of phenolphthalein indicator are added to the potassium iodide (KI) solution and an electric current is then passed through the solution. Phenolphthalein indicator is colourless in acidic solution and pink in basic solution.
- The cathode reaction is reduction.

$$2H_2O + 2e^- \longrightarrow H_2 + 2OH^-$$

The solution is pink as the solution is alkaline.

- The anode reaction is oxidation.

$$2I^- \longrightarrow I_2 + 2e^-$$

A brown colour is noted at the anode as iodine is produced when iodide ions lose electrons and are oxidised.

Electroplating

Electroplating is a process where electrolysis is used to put a layer of one metal on another.

Example: Coating a nickel spoon with silver

Procedure

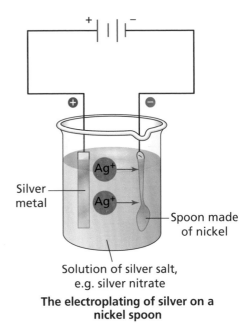

The electroplating of silver on a nickel spoon

- Set up apparatus as shown and pass an electric current through the silver nitrate solution.
- Cathode reaction:

$$Ag^+ \; + \; e^- \; \longrightarrow \; Ag$$

Silver ions receive electrons to become silver atoms which plate out on nickel electrode.

- Anode reaction:

$$Ag \; \longrightarrow \; Ag^+ \; + \; e^-$$

Silver anode slowly dissolves in the solution forming silver ions.

Conditions needed for electroplating to occur

- The object to be plated must be connected to the cathode.
- The electrolyte must be a salt of the metal that is being plated onto object.
- The anode must be the same metal that is being plated.

Uses of electroplating

- In cutlery and jewellery.
- To protect against corrosion e.g. chromium plating of bath fittings.

Oxidation number

HL

The oxidation number of an atom or ion is the charge that the atom or ion has if the electrons are distributed according to certain rules.

Rules for oxidation numbers

- The oxidation number of an alkali metal (Group I) in a compound is $+1$.
- The oxidation number of alkaline earth-metals (Group II) in its compounds is $+2$.
- The sum of all the oxidation numbers of all the atoms in a neutral molecule is zero,

e.g. magnesium oxide: $\quad$ MgO

$$(+2)(-2) = 0$$

- In free elements each atom has an oxidation number of zero,

e.g. bromine $\quad (Br_2)$

$$2(0)$$

Hydrogen in a compound has an oxidation number of $+1$, except in metal hydrides where it is -1.

A metal hydride is a compound of a metal and hydrogen,

e.g. sodium hydride $\quad (NaH)$

$$(+1)(-1) = 0$$

- The oxidation number of oxygen in a compound is -2.

Exceptions:

(i) Peroxides, where it is -1,

e.g. hydrogen peroxide: $\quad H_2O_2$

$$2(+1)2(-1)$$

(ii) If oxygen is bonded with fluorine, which is more electronegative, it has an oxidation number of $+2$,

e.g. $\quad OF_2$

$$(+2)2(-1)$$

- For simple ions the oxidation number is the same as the charge on the ion, e.g. calcium ion (Ca^{2+}) where the oxidation number is $+2$.
- The sum of all the oxidation numbers of all the atoms in a complex ion is equal to the charge on the ion.

Sample exam question: 2006 Q10(b) Higher level

What is the oxidation number of nitrogen in NO_3^-? $\qquad$ **(3 marks)**

Solution

NO_3^-

$$(X)3(-2) = -1$$

$$\text{Oxidation number of N} = X = +5 \qquad \text{(3 marks)}$$

- The oxidation number of a halogen is -1 when bonded to a less electronegative atom.

Examples: (i) Hydrogen chloride $\quad$ HCl

$$(+1)(-1)$$

(ii) $\qquad Cl_2O$

$$2(+1)(-2)$$

Here the oxidation number of Cl is $+1$ as oxygen is more electronegative. Fluorine always has an oxidation number of -1 as it is the most electronegative element.

- Fractional oxidation numbers do exist.

  Example: the oxidation no. of sulfur in $Na_2S_4O_6$ is 2.5

$$Na_2S_4O_6$$
$$2(+1) + 4(2.5) + 6(-2) = 0$$

Oxidation and reduction in terms of oxidation number

key definition

Oxidation is an increase in oxidation number. Reduction is a decrease in oxidation number.

Sample exam question: 2002 Q10(a)(i)(ii) Higher level

(i) Using oxidation numbers identify what species is being oxidised and what species is being reduced in the following reaction:

$$MnO_4^- + Cl^- + H^+ \longrightarrow Mn^{2+} + Cl_2 + H_2O \quad \text{(12 marks)}$$

(ii) Hence or otherwise balance the equation. (9 marks)

Solution

(i) *Identifying the species*

$$MnO_4^- \quad + \quad Cl^- \quad + \quad H^+ \quad \longrightarrow \quad Mn^{2+} \quad + \quad Cl_2 \quad + \quad H_2O$$
$$(+7)4(-2) \qquad -1 \qquad +1 \quad \longrightarrow \quad +2 \qquad \quad 2(0) \qquad 2(+1)(-2)$$

Mn is reduced as its oxidation number is decreased by 5:

$$\text{Mn:} \quad +7 \longrightarrow +2 \quad \text{(6 marks)}$$

Cl is oxidised as its oxidation number is increased by 1;

$$Cl^- \longrightarrow Cl \quad \text{(6 marks)}$$
$$-1 \qquad \quad 0$$

(ii) *Balancing the equation*

Step 1: Balance the change in oxidation number
Step 2: Balance the overall reaction.

- To balance the change in oxidation number multiply Cl^- by 5:

$$MnO_4^- + 5Cl^- + H^+ \longrightarrow Mn^{2+} + 2\tfrac{1}{2}Cl_2 + H_2O$$

- Balance the equation (leave H^+ till last):

$$MnO_4^- + 5Cl^- + 8H^+ \longrightarrow Mn^{2+} + 2\tfrac{1}{2}Cl_2 + 4H_2O \quad \text{(9 marks)}$$

22 Option 1: Industrial and Atmospheric Chemistry

 To revise the following:

- **Option 1A: Industrial chemistry**
  - (a) Contribution of chemistry to society
  - (b) Types of industrial chemical processes
  - (c) Characteristics of effective industrial processes
  - (d) Industrial case study: manufacture of magnesium oxide from sea water
- **Option 1B: Atmospheric chemistry**
  - (a) Oxygen and nitrogen gases
  - (b) Oxides of carbon including carbon dioxide
  - (c) Carbon dioxide in water
  - (d) The carbon cycle
  - (e) Greenhouse effect
  - (f) Ozone layer

Option 1A: Industrial chemistry

Contributions of chemistry to society

- Agriculture e.g. fertilisers and herbicides to increase crop yields.
- Health e.g. medicines.
- Household products e.g. cleaning products, toiletries, etc.
- Materials such as plastics, metals, fuels, etc.

Types of industrial chemical processes

- A batch process is an industrial process where the raw materials are fed into a reaction vessel and allowed to react for a certain time and the product formed is removed. The process is then repeated with a new lot of reactants.
- A continuous process is an industrial process where the feedstock or raw materials are continually fed in at one end of the reaction vessel and then removed from the other end.
- A semi-continuous process is a combination of a batch process and a continuous process. The batch process comes first.

Advantages and disadvantages of batch process

Advantages of batch process	Disadvantages of batch process
1. Capital costs of building plant are low as small quantities are involved	1. Labour intensive e.g. filling and emptying vessel
2. Same vessel can be used for a range of products	2. Contamination of one batch with another is possible

Advantages and disadvantages of continuous process

Advantages of continuous process	Disadvantages of continuous process
1. Suitable for large scale production of materials	1. Capital costs are high to build large plant
2. Low risk of contamination	2. Limited to one type of product

Characteristics of effective industrial processes

- **Feedstock:** this consists of the reactants needed for the process. It is produced by purifying the raw materials.
- **Reaction rate:** the best conditions of temperature, pressure and catalyst are chosen for the reaction to occur at the optimum rate. These reaction conditions must be economical to maintain.
- **Product yield:** the reaction conditions chosen must result in a satisfactory yield of product e.g. in an equilibrium situation such as the production of ammonia by the Haber process.

- **Co-products:** these are other products formed along with the main product. These products have to be separated from the main product. If they are useful they can be sold or used on site. If they are not useful they must be disposed of.
- **Waste disposal and effluent control:** costs are involved in ensuring that gas and waste water emissions from the plant are not harmful to the environment.
- **Quality control:** the use of instrumentation in quality control is often used to ensure the product is of the highest quality.
- **Safety:** health and safety regulations must be rigorously enforced e.g. the site will have a first aid centre and staff will be trained in first aid and fire prevention.
- **Costs:**
  - (a) Fixed costs which have to be paid regardless of the rate of production e.g. labour cost.
  - (b) Variable costs depend directly on the rate of output of the plant e.g. cost of raw materials, electricity, fuel, etc.

  Cost reductions methods include recycling heat and using catalysts.
- **Site location:** the location of an industrial site must take into account such things as:
  - (i) the availability of water and electricity
  - (ii) good road or rail connections for transport
  - (iii) source of raw materials.
- **Plant construction materials:** the construction materials in a plant should be generally unreactive and resistant to corrosion e.g. stainless steel.

Industrial case study: Manufacture of magnesium oxide (Periclase) from sea water

- Magnesium oxide (periclase) is produced from sea water by Premier Periclase in Drogheda. Periclase has a high melting point and being heat-resistant it is used to make bricks to line furnaces and smelters.
- The type of process is continuous where the raw materials are continuously fed into reactor and product periclase removed.
- The raw materials used here are sea water and limestone.

Formation of feedstock from the raw materials

- The sea water is purified by removing sand and other particles by allowing the sea water to settle in large reservoirs. Carbon dioxide is also removed from the water.
- The limestone is crushed and washed before being heated in a large oven to form calcium oxide or quicklime.

Reactions to produce calcium oxide or periclase from sea water and limestone

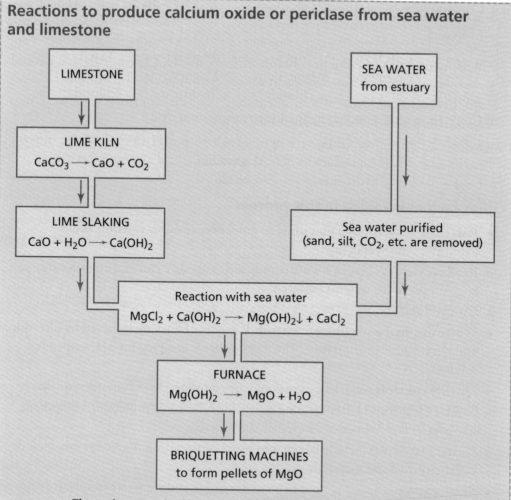

The main stages in the production of magnesium oxide (periclase)

There are four main stages in the conversion of limestone and sea water into magnesium oxide.

1. Conversion of limestone to lime.

Here the limestone is heated in a large oven or kiln:

$$CaCO_3 \xrightarrow{\text{heat}} CaO + CO_2$$
$$\text{Limestone} \qquad \text{Calcium oxide} \atop \text{(quicklime)}$$

2. Conversion of quicklime to slaked lime (calcium hydroxide).

Here water is added to the quicklime:

$$CaO + H_2O \longrightarrow Ca(OH)_2$$
$$\text{Quicklime} \qquad \text{Slaked lime} \atop \text{(calcium hydroxide)}$$

3. Slaked lime reacts with magnesium chloride in sea water to produce magnesium hydroxide as:

$$Ca(OH)_2 + MgCl_2 \longrightarrow Mg(OH)_2 + CaCl_2$$

Slaked lime   Magnesium   Magnesium   Calcium

chloride   hydroxide   chloride

4. Conversion of magnesium hydroxide to magnesium oxide

$$Mg(OH)_2 \longrightarrow MgO + H_2O$$

Magnesium   Magnesium

hydroxide   oxide

Other factors involved in this process

- **Rate:** The conversion of limestone to quicklime is a slow reaction and determines the overall rate.
- **Product yield:** A litre of sea water only yields about 2 g of magnesium oxide so a large supply of sea water is required.
- **Co-products:** None.
- **Waste disposal and effluent control:** Particles of dust are removed by filtration and electrostatic precipitators. The waste water is analysed for pH, suspended solids etc.
- **Quality control:** Acid/base titrations carried out to check limestone quality.
- **Safety:** Health and safety training is provided. Personal protection equipment like goggles and helmets are supplied as required.
- **Costs:** Fixed costs include labour and plant depreciation. Variable costs include electricity, fuel and materials.
- **Site location:** The site is close to good limestone and sea water supply. It is also convenient for road, rail and sea transport.
- **Plant construction materials:** The building is made of steel with iron cladding. The reactors are made of concrete.

Option 1B: Atmospheric chemistry

The atmosphere is a layer of gas that stretches about 100 km above the surface of the Earth. The composition of air is given in the following table.

Name of gas	Percentage in air
Oxygen	21%
Nitrogen	78%
Carbon dioxide	0.03%
Noble gases	<1%
Water vapour	Variable

Oxygen

Oxygen is the most reactive gas in air.

Uses of oxygen

(i) It is used with ethyne in blow torches for welding.

(ii) It is also used in steel making and in hospitals for patients with breathing problems.

Nitrogen

- Nitrogen is a very stable element with a strong triple covalent bond and is chemically unreactive.

Uses of nitrogen

- It is used to keep foods fresh inside packaging e.g. crisps.
- It is used to make ammonia for fertilisers (Haber process).
- Liquid nitrogen is produced industrially as described by liquefaction and distillation of air. The liquid nitrogen is used to:
  (i) freeze foods
  (ii) remove warts.

Production of oxygen and nitrogen in industry

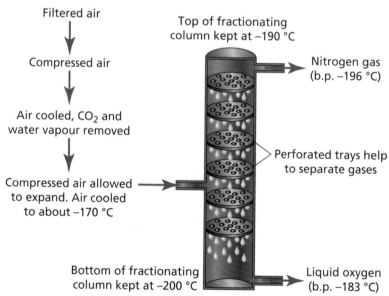

Industrial production of oxygen and nitrogen by the liquefaction and fractional distillation of the air

- Oxygen and nitrogen gases are produced industrially by liquefaction and distillation of air.
- Liquefaction means that the air is cooled to a liquid at very low temperatures ($-200\,°C$). The liquefaction of the air is achieved by compressing and then cooling it.
- Carbon dioxide and water vapour are removed at this stage as they would solidify later and block pipes.
- The liquefied air is then fed into a fractionating column as shown in the diagram. The liquid oxygen and liquid nitrogen are separated at different levels due to their different boiling points.

key definition

Nitrogen fixation is converting nitrogen gas into compounds that can be used by plants e.g. nitrates.

There are two main natural methods of nitrogen fixation.

1. Nitrogen-fixing bacteria in the soil or in the roots of peas and beans convert nitrogen gas in the soil into nitrates for plants to take into their roots. The plants use these nitrates to make protein for growth.
2. Lightning provides the energy for the following reactions in the atmosphere during a thunderstorm:

    (i) formation of nitrogen monoxide

    $$N_2 \;+\; O_2 \longrightarrow \underset{\substack{\text{Nitrogen}\\\text{monoxide}}}{2NO}$$

    (ii) subsequent formation of nitrogen dioxide

    $$NO \;+\; \tfrac{1}{2}O_2 \longrightarrow \underset{\substack{\text{Nitrogen}\\\text{dioxide}}}{NO_2}$$

    (iii) Nitrogen dioxide dissolves in rain water to form nitrous acid (HNO_2) and nitric acid (HNO_3) as:

    $$2NO_2 \;+\; H_2O \longrightarrow HNO_2 \;+\; HNO_3$$

    The nitric acid in the rain water forms nitrates in the soil which are taken up by plants.

The nitrogen cycle

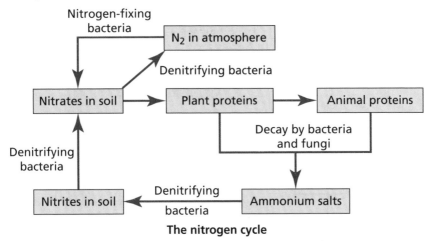

The nitrogen cycle

The above diagram demonstrates the different ways nitrogen gas is used to produce nitrogen in the soil e.g. nitrogen fixation by lightning and nitrogen-fixing bacteria. It also describes the different ways nitrogen is returned to the atmosphere by denitrifying bacteria which convert nitrates into nitrogen gas.

Oxides of carbon

Carbon dioxide (CO_2) and carbon monoxide (CO)

- When carbon is burned in excess oxygen carbon dioxide is formed as:

$$C + O_2 \longrightarrow CO_2$$

- Carbon dioxide is an acidic gas .Therefore it lowers the pH in water and turns universal indicator a pink colour.
- Carbon dioxide dissolves in water to produce:

(i) carbonic acid as:

$$CO_2 + H_2O \longrightarrow H_2CO_3 \text{ (carbonic acid)}$$

(ii) the carbonate and the hydrogen carbonate ion.

The carbonic acid formed in water is a weak acid and can dissociate to a small extent to form the carbonate ion(CO_3^{2-}) or the hydrogen carbonate ion.

(a) $H_2CO_3 \rightleftharpoons H^+ + HCO_3^-$
Hydrogen carbonate
ion

(b) $H_2CO_3 \rightleftharpoons 2H^+ + CO_3^{2-}$
Carbonate ion

- Carbon dioxide is produced in industry as a co-product of ethanol in the fermentation of glucose using yeast enzymes.

$$C_6H_{12}O_6 \longrightarrow 2CO_2 + 2C_2H_5OH$$
$$\text{Glucose} \qquad\qquad \text{Ethanol}$$

- Carbon dioxide is used in fire extinguishers and fizzy drinks.
- Carbon monoxide is formed when carbon is burned in a limited supply of oxygen.

$$C + \tfrac{1}{2}O_2 \longrightarrow CO \text{ (carbon monoxide)}$$

Carbon monoxide is a colourless gas with no smell. It is a poisonous gas and can lead to fatalities when a fuel is being burned in a confined space where there is a lack of oxygen.

The carbon cycle

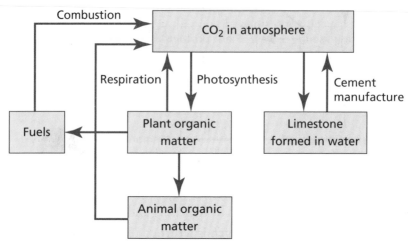

The carbon cycle

- The carbon cycle demonstrates the ways in which the level of carbon dioxide in the atmosphere does not change greatly.
- Carbon dioxide is produced for example by burning fossil fuels and by respiration of plants and animals.
- Carbon dioxide is removed from the atmosphere by photosynthesis of plants and also by being dissolved in rain water and the oceans.

The greenhouse effect and global warming

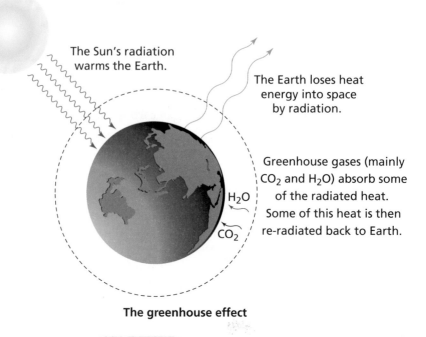

The greenhouse effect

The greenhouse effect is the trapping of the Sun's heat energy by some gases in the atmosphere.

- The Earth's atmosphere acts like a greenhouse. Short ultraviolet rays from the sun are allowed to pass through the atmosphere and are absorbed by the Earth.
- The Earth heats up and radiates heat back out in the form of long infra-red rays. However, gases in the atmosphere do not allow this heat to escape. This causes an increase in Earth's temperature.
- The main greenhouse gases are carbon dioxide and water vapour. Other significant greenhouse gases are methane, chlorofluorocarbons (CFCs) and nitrogen(I) oxide (N_2O).
- The greenhouse factor measures the greenhouse effect caused by a gas relative to the same amount of carbon dioxide which is given a value of 1. The greenhouse factor therefore compares the greenhouse effect of different gases in the atmosphere e.g. CFCs have the biggest greenhouse factor. The following table summarises the greenhouse factor of the main greenhouse gases.

Greenhouse gas	Source	Greenhouse factor
CFCs	Aerosols	21000–25000
Nitrogen(I) oxide (N_2O)	Car exhausts	160
Methane	Cattle, landfills	30
Carbon dioxide	Burning fossil fuels	1
Water vapour	Evaporation of seas, oceans	0.1

Enhanced greenhouse effect

- Increased concentrations of greenhouse gases, particularly carbon dioxide, are causing the Earth to get warmer.
- This extra warming due to the enhanced greenhouse effect is called global warming.
- Human activity has played a large role in this by increased burning of fossil fuels and the removal of large forests.
- The possible effects of global warming are:
  (i) melting of polar ice caps leading to increased sea levels and flooding
  (ii) more violent storms.

Atmospheric pollution

Air pollution exists when there is a constituent in air present to such an extent that there is a significant risk to present or future health or the environment.

Acid rain

Acid rain is rain with a pH of less than 5.5.

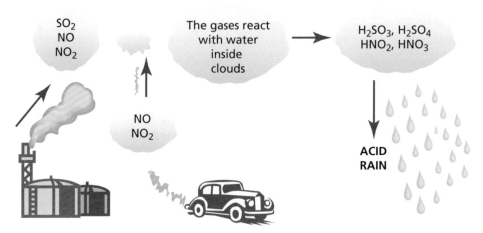

The formation of acid rain in the atmosphere

Causes of acid rain
- Oxides of sulfur e.g. sulfur dioxide (SO_2) and sulfur trioxide (SO_3).
- Oxides of nitrogen e.g. nitrogen dioxide (NO_2) and nitrogen monoxide (NO).

Harmful effects of acid rain
1. Corrosion of limestone buildings and metal.
2. Causes aluminium to be leached out of the soil into rivers and lakes which causes fish to die.
3. Causes damage to trees.

Oxides of sulfur
- Sulfur dioxide is formed from the burning of sulfur in fossil fuels and volcanic emissions. The reaction is:
$$S \; + \; O_2 \; \longrightarrow \; SO_2 \, (\text{sulfur dioxide})$$
- Sulfur dioxide is an acidic oxide and dissolves in water to form sulfurous acid.
$$SO_2 \; + \; H_2O \; \longrightarrow \; H_2SO_3 \, (\text{sulfurous acid})$$
- Sulfur dioxide is oxidised by oxygen in the air to sulfur trioxide (SO_3).
$$SO_2 \; + \; \tfrac{1}{2}O_2 \; \longrightarrow \; SO_3 \, (\text{sulfur trioxide})$$
- Sulfur trioxide dissolves in water to form sulfuric acid.
$$SO_3 \; + \; H_2O \; \longrightarrow \; H_2SO_4 \, (\text{sulfuric acid})$$
- Both sulfurous and sulfuric acid contribute to acid rain.

Oxides of nitrogen

- Oxides of nitrogen are produced at high temperatures from car exhausts and power stations. The nitrogen gas reacts with oxygen in the air to form nitrogen monoxide initially.

$$N_2 + O_2 \longrightarrow 2NO \text{ (nitrogen monoxide)}$$

- The nitrogen monoxide reacts with oxygen in the air to produce nitrogen dioxide.

$$NO + \tfrac{1}{2}O_2 \longrightarrow NO_2 \text{ (nitrogen dioxide).}$$

- The nitrogen dioxide then dissolves in water to form a mixture of nitrous and nitric acid.

$$2NO_2 + H_2O \longrightarrow \underset{\text{Nitrous acid}}{HNO_2} + \underset{\text{Nitric acid}}{HNO_3}$$

Scrubbing of waste gases from power stations

Limestone is used in the chimneys of power stations to remove sulfur dioxide. The following reaction occurs:

$$\underset{\text{Limestone}}{CaCO_3} + \underset{\text{Sulfur dioxide}}{SO_2} \longrightarrow \underset{\text{Calcium sulfite}}{CaSO_3} + \underset{\text{Carbon dioxide}}{CO_2}$$

The ozone layer

- Ozone has the molecular formula O_3. There is a layer of ozone at about 25 km above the Earth's surface.
- Ozone acts as a sunscreen as it absorbs the harmful ultraviolet radiation in the Sun's rays. This ultraviolet radiation causes sunburn and can cause skin cancer.

Formation of ozone

(HL)

Ozone is formed in the upper part of the atmosphere called the stratosphere by the following two reactions:

(i) breakdown of oxygen by light energy (photodissociation)

$$O_2 \xrightarrow{\text{Sunlight}} \underset{\text{Oxygen free radicals}}{O^{\cdot} + O^{\cdot}}$$

(ii) oxygen molecules and the very reactive oxygen free radicals combine as follows to form ozone.

$$O_2 + O^{\cdot} \longrightarrow O_3 \text{ (ozone)}$$

Photodissociation of ozone

Here ultraviolet light from the Sun is absorbed by ozone and the formation reaction of ozone above is reversed.

$$O_3 \longrightarrow O_2 + O^{\cdot}$$

Most of the oxygen atoms formed in this reaction react with oxygen molecules again to re-form ozone.

Damage to the ozone layer

- Damage to the ozone layer is caused by the presence of chlorofluorocarbons (CFCs) in the atmosphere. In the upper atmosphere or stratosphere the CFCs break down and release chlorine atoms which attack ozone.

  One example of a reaction in which a CFC is broken down is:

$$CCl_3F \longrightarrow CCl_2F + Cl^{\cdot}$$

  Trichlorofluoromethane

  The chlorine free radical produced reacts with ozone.

$$Cl^{\cdot} + O_3 \longrightarrow O_2 + ClO^{\cdot}$$

  Chlorine oxide

  The chlorine oxide radical now reacts with oxygen free radicals as:

$$ClO + O^{\cdot} \longrightarrow Cl^{\cdot} + O_2$$

  More chlorine free radicals are released by this reaction to attack further ozone molecules.

- The sources of CFCs are aerosol cans, fridges and air conditioning units.
- CFCs are produced from alkanes by substitution reactions. Examples of CFCs are dichlorodifluoromethane (CCl_2F_2) and trichlorofluoromethane (CCl_3F).
- Effects of damage to the ozone layer are:
  (i) more harmful ultraviolet rays reach the Earth, leading to sunburn and skin cancer
  (ii) eye damage and damage to plants.
- The use of CFCs is now banned and they have been replaced by hydrofluorocarbons or hydrochlorofluorocarbons which are less damaging to the ozone layer.

23 Option 2: Materials, Electrochemistry and Extraction of Metals

aims To revise the following:

Option 2A: Materials
- Crystals and crystal types
- Allotropes of carbon e.g. Buckminsterfullerene
- Addition polymers
- Polymers of substituted alkenes
- Discovery of poly(ethene)
- Discovery of Teflon
- Recycling of plastics
- Metals
- Alloys

Option 2B: Electrochemistry and extraction of metals
- The electrochemical series
- Electrolysis of molten salts
- Corrosion and its prevention
- Extraction of sodium metal
- Extraction of aluminium
- Anodising
- Transition metals
- Iron and steel production

Option 2A: Materials

Crystals and crystal types

key definition

A crystal is a solid particle with a regular shape and consists of faces intersecting at definite angles. There is an orderly array of particles within the crystal.

A solid without a crystal structure is said to be amorphous (without order) e.g. glass, rubber.

X-Ray crystallography

- The regular array within crystals was first determined by William and Lawrence Bragg in 1915. They used X-rays to show the arrangement of particles within crystals. They became the only father and son team to win the Nobel Prize. They won it for their work on the crystal structure of sodium chloride.
- Another important person in the area of X-ray crystallography was Dorothy Hodgkin who determined the structure of the complex organic molecule Vitamin B_{12} in 1964. She was also part of a team that discovered the structure of penicillin.

Types of crystal

Crystals are classified according to the units that occupy the lattice points.

Ionic and molecular crystals

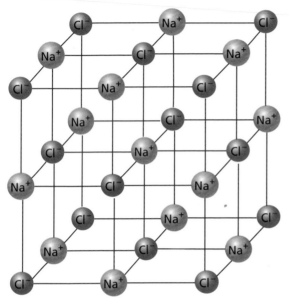

The ionic crystal structure of sodium chloride

Ionic crystals have ions at the lattice points e.g. NaCl, KI, MgO. The lattice is held together by the electrostatic attraction of positive and negative ions.

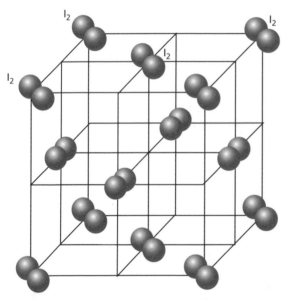

The molecular crystal structure of iodine

Molecular crystals have molecules at the lattice points e.g. iodine. Weak van der Waals forces hold the lattice together which explains the low melting point of iodine.

Covalent macromolecular crystals

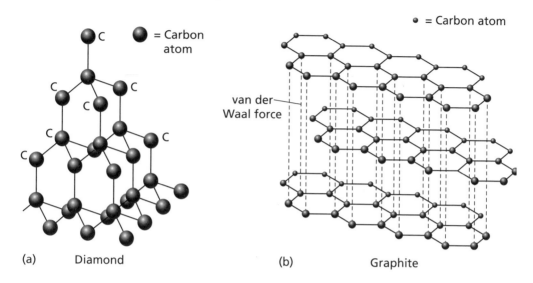

(a) Diamond

(b) Graphite

Covalent macromolecular crystals have atoms at the lattice points and these atoms are joined by covalent bonds in a giant interlocking network.

Diamond, graphite and buckminsterfullerene are examples of covalent macromolecular crystals. They are also allotropes of carbon.

- Diamond is the hardest material known to man and is used in diamond cutting and oil drilling. The reason for its hardness is that each carbon atom is covalently bonded to four other carbon atoms in a giant network of atoms, as in diagram.

key definition

Allotropes are different physical forms of the same element.

- Graphite, on the other hand a much softer material than diamond and is used, for example, as the 'lead' in pencils. The reason for this is that the crystal of graphite consists of layers of carbon atoms. The bonding within each layer is very strong as the atoms are joined by covalent bonds. However, the layers are only held together by weak van der Waals forces and are easy to separate. This explains why graphite can be used in pencils and as a lubricant.

  Graphite can also conduct electricity as only three carbon atoms are involved in bonding and therefore there is a 'spare' electron that is free to move and therefore conduct electricity. Graphite is the only non-metal that conducts an electric current.

- Buckminsterfullerene is another allotrope of carbon. It consists of clusters of football shaped molecules. Each molecule is made up of 60 carbon atoms joined by covalent bonds.

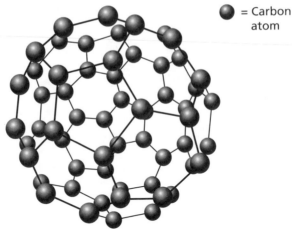

= Carbon atom

Buckminsterfullerene

Metallic crystals

Positive ions

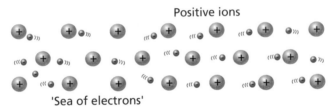

'Sea of electrons'

Structure of a metallic crystal

Metallic crystals have their lattice points occupied by positive metal ions. These metal ions have lost one or more electron and these electrons are free to move over the positive metal ions forming a sea of electrons.

A metallic bond is set up where the attraction between the positive metal ions and the sea of electrons holds the metal together.

The sea of electrons present in a metal explains the good electrical conductivity of metals as they are free to move from one end of the metal to the other.

The binding forces of different types of crystal are summarised in the following table:

Type of crystal	Example	Unit occupying the lattice points	Binding force
Ionic	NaCl	Positive and negative ions	Ionic bond
Molecular (non-polar)	Iodine (I_2)	Molecules	van der Waals
Molecular (polar)	HCl, ice	Molecules	HCl: dipole–dipole attraction ice: hydrogen bonds
Covalent macromolecular	Diamond, graphite	Atom	Covalent bonds (sometimes with van der Waals forces)
Metallic	Sodium, iron, aluminium	Positive metal ions	Metallic bond

The properties of the different types of crystals are compared in the following table:

Type of crystal	Strength	Melting point	Electrical conductivity	Solubility
Ionic	Hard but brittle	High	Conducts electricity when melted or in solution	Usually soluble in polar solvents e.g. water but not soluble in non-polar solvents
Molecular	Usually weak	Low	Do not conduct	Varies with the crystal
Covalent (macromolecular)	Usually hard	High	Do not conduct except for graphite	Insoluble in polar solvents
Metallic	Can be hard or soft depending on metal e.g. sodium is soft but iron is hard	Variable depending on metal	Good conductors	Insoluble usually in polar or non-polar solvents

Polymers and addition polymers

A polymer is a long chain molecule which is composed of many repeating units of a small molecule or monomer.

Addition polymers

Alkenes undergo addition reactions because of their double bond. Therefore alkenes are the monomers or basic units in the manufacture of polymers which are used in the manufacture of plastics.

Poly(ethene)

The polymer poly(ethene) is produced by subjecting ethene to high pressure and heat in the presence of a catalyst.

Ethene $\xrightarrow{\text{Heat, pressure, catalyst}}$

Formation of poly(ethene) from ethene

There were two types of poly(ethene) produced.

- Low density poly(ethene) was initially produced in 1933 by the British chemists Eric Fawcett and Reginald Gibson. It was soft and flexible as the chains of carbon atoms had a lot of branches and there was of lot of empty space between them. This type of soft poly(ethene) was used in insulating electric wires and plastic bags.

- High density poly(ethene) was produced later in 1953 by Karl Ziegler. Using certain catalysts (organometallics e.g. $Al(C_2H_5)_3$) he was able to produce poly(ethene) with little branching and so the molecules were packed closer together giving a higher density material.

High density poly(ethene) is used in buckets, basins and bottle crates.

Poly(chloroethene) or polyvinyl chloride (PVC)

The polymer poly(chloroethene) is produced from chloroethene (vinyl chloride).

Chloroethene $\xrightarrow{\text{Heat, pressure, catalyst}}$ Poly(chloroethene) = PVC

Formation of poly(vinylchloride)

Polarisation of the C–Cl bond means that there is dipole–dipole attraction between the polymer chains which makes PVC a strong rigid plastic. It can therefore be used in windows and gutters.

However, a softer type of PVC can also be formed using plasticisers. Plasticisers are small molecules that fit between the polymer chains and allow them to slide over each other making the polymer softer.

This softened type of PVC is used in raincoats and shower curtains.

Poly(propene) or polypropylene

Poly(propene) is prepared by the polymerisation of propene.

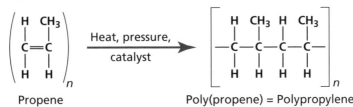

Formation of poly(propene)

This polymer was made using Ziegler catalysts and is a high-density material. It is used in making ropes, chairs, toys, buckets, etc.

Poly(phenylethene) (Also known as polystyrene)

The polymer poly(phenylethene) is prepared by the polymerisation of phenylethene.

Formation of poly(phenylethene)

There are two types of polystyrene:
- rigid polystyrene: used to make flower pots, yogurt pots, cases for CDs, etc
- expanded polystyrene(made by adding hexane): egg boxes, burger boxes, etc.

Poly(tetrafluoroethene) or teflon

This polymer is produced from tetrafluoroethene

Formation of poly(tetrafluoroethene)

Teflon was discovered in 1938 by Roy Plunkett and is a soft plastic inert to acids and bases and resistant to high temperatures.

Teflon is used in non-stick frying pans, plumber's tape and body implants in medicine.

Recycling of plastics

- Thermosetting plastics can be recycled as they can be softened by heating and remoulded e.g. polystyrene.
- Thermosetting plastics like bakelite cannot be recycled as they cannot be softened by heating and cannot be remoulded.

When plastics, e.g. expanded polystyrene, are recycled they go through the following stages:

- sorting: separated from each other by hand
- shredding: chopped into small pieces by a granulator
- washing: the plastic is washed with steam and detergent to remove any impurities
- drying: warm air is used to remove any excess water
- re-extrusion: the dried shredded plastic is fed into a machine called an extruder where it is melted and remoulded.

Option 2B: Electrochemistry and the extraction of metals

Comparison of metals and non-metals

The properties of metals and non-metals are compared in the following table.

Physical properties of metals	Physical properties of non-metals
Most metals are hard	Some solid non-metals are hard but brittle
Metals are good conductors of heat and electricity	Non-metals are not good conductors
Most metals have a lustre or 'shine'	Non-metals do not have a lustre
Metals are malleable, i.e. can be hammered into shape e.g. lead	Non-metals are not malleable
Metals are ductile, i.e. can be drawn into wires e.g. copper	Non-metals are not ductile

Alloys

key definition

An alloy is a mixture of two or more elements at least one of which is a metal.

Some examples of alloys are given in the table below.

Alloy	Constituent elements	Property change
Steel	Iron and carbon	Harder and tougher
Brass	Copper and zinc	Harder and different colour
Bronze	Copper and tin	Harder

Early contributors to electrochemistry of metals

- In 1791 Luigi Galvani discovered that the muscles in a dissected frog's leg twitched when touched by two different metals. He thought that the twitching was due to some property of the living tissue of the frog.
- In 1794 Alessandro Volta showed that electricity is generated when two different metals are placed in a conducting solution. Volta was the first person to construct a battery using copper and zinc plates separated by cardboard moistened with salt solution. It was called the Voltaic pile.
- In the early 1800s Humphrey Davy improved on the voltaic pile and used more powerful batteries to isolate sodium and potassium metals by electrolysis.
- Michael Faraday, an assistant of Davy, went on to discover the laws of electrolysis as well as inventing the electric motor and generator.

The electrochemical series of metals

key definition

The electrochemical series of metals is a series of metals listed in order of their ability to lose electrons (electrode potential).

Electrochemical series		
Potassium	K	Very reactive
Calcium	Ca	
Sodium	Na	
Magnesium	Mg	
Aluminium	Al	
Zinc	Zn	
Iron	Fe	
Lead	Pb	
*Hydrogen	H	
Copper	Cu	
Silver	Ag	
Gold	Au	Least reactive

Memory aid (top to bottom): Poor Chaotic Student Makes A Zillion Improvements Learning His Chemistry Success Guide!

Elements at the top of the list e.g. potassium and calcium have a great tendency to lose electrons and be oxidised. Therefore they are very reactive.

Corrosion of metals

- Corrosion of metals is caused by the action of water, air and other chemicals such as acids on the metal surface.

> **key definition**
>
> Corrosion is any undesired process where a metal is converted into one of its compounds.

- Metals higher up in the electrochemical series generally corrode faster than those lower down. Aluminium is an exception to this as aluminium forms a layer of oxide on its surface which prevents further corrosion.
- The most common example of corrosion is that of the rusting of iron or steel. Rusting requires the presence of water or oxygen.

Prevention of corrosion

- Painting and greasing.
- Galvanising: this involves coating iron or steel with zinc. Zinc is higher up in the electrochemical series and so it reacts with air or oxygen in preference to the iron or steel.
- Plating with another metal e.g. iron or steel can be coated with an unreactive metal like tin in tin cans. Chromium is also used to protect car bumpers.
- Alloying: iron is mixed with chromium and carbon to form stainless steel which is very resistant to corrosion.
- Sacrificial anodes: this is similar to galvanising as the iron is placed in contact with another element which is more reactive e.g. large pieces of zinc or magnesium are attached to the steel hulls of ships or underground pipes. The zinc or magnesium reacts in preference to the iron or steel. The zinc in this case is the anode and is eaten away whereas the hull of the ship is the cathode and does not corrode. This method of protection is also called cathodic protection as steel is being protected by making it the cathode.

Electrolysis of molten salts

Electrolysis of molten lead bromide(PbBr₂)

In the electrolysis of molten lead bromide using inert carbon electrodes lead is formed at the cathode and bromine is formed at the anode.

Cathode (−) reaction: reduction occurs at the cathode

$$Pb^{2+} + 2e^- \longrightarrow Pb \quad \text{(lead is produced at the cathode)}$$

Anode (+) reaction: oxidation at the anode

$$2Br^- \longrightarrow Br_2 + 2e^- \quad \text{(bromine produced at the anode)}$$

The overall reaction is: $Pb^{2+} + 2Br^- \longrightarrow Pb + Br_2$

Memory aid: **red cat**.

Extraction of sodium from molten sodium chloride

Very reactive elements like sodium located at the top of the electrochemical series have a great tendency to lose electrons. Their ores or salts are very stable and only electrolysis can be used to separate them.

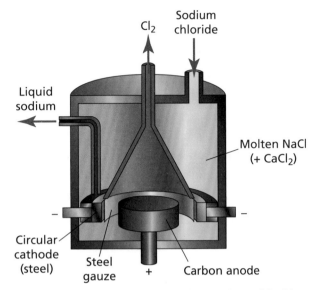

Extraction of sodium from molten sodium chloride (Downs cell)

- The Downs cell is used to extract sodium from sodium chloride. The sodium chloride is mixed with calcium chloride to lower the melting point. A large electric current is passed through the molten electrolyte.
- Cathode reaction: $Na^+ + e^- \longrightarrow Na$ (sodium produced)
- Anode reaction: $Cl^- \longrightarrow \frac{1}{2}Cl_2 + e^-$ (chlorine produced)
  Overall reaction: $NaCl \longrightarrow Na + \frac{1}{2}Cl_2$
- A steel gauze is used to separate the anode from the cathode. This prevents the sodium formed at the cathode from reacting with the chlorine formed at the anode.
- Uses of the products of electrolysis:
  (i) sodium: street lighting, coolant in nuclear reactors
  (ii) chlorine: water treatment, disinfectant, making polymers (PVC).

Extraction of aluminium from bauxite

Aluminium is extracted from the ore bauxite which contains about 50 percent alumina or aluminium oxide (Al_2O_3).
There are two stages in the extraction of aluminium from bauxite:

1. aluminium oxide is removed from bauxite
2. aluminium is separated from aluminium oxide by electrolysis.

Stage 1: Separating aluminium oxide from bauxite

- **Crushing and mixing:** the bauxite is crushed and mixed with hot sodium hydroxide solution. It is crushed so that it reacts faster.
- **Digestion:** the hydrated aluminium oxide reacts with sodium hydroxide as follows:
  $$Al_2O_3.3H_2O + 2NaOH \longrightarrow 2NaAlO_2 + 4H_2O$$
  Hydrated aluminium oxide   Sodium aluminate
- **Clarification (removal of impurities):** flour is added to remove impurities such as oxides of iron and this precipitates out as 'red mud'.

- **Precipitation of aluminium oxide:** The sodium aluminate solution is pumped to clean tanks where it is cooled and seed crystals of $Al_2O_3.3H_2O$ are added to speed up crystal formation:

$$2NaAlO_2 \;+\; 4H_2O \longrightarrow Al_2O_3.3H_2O \;+\; 2NaOH$$

> Memory aid: this reaction is the reverse of the digestion reaction on the previous page.

- **Removal of water of crystallisation:** the hydrated aluminium oxide is roasted in a rotary kiln and a pure white powder of aluminium oxide is formed as:

$$Al_2O_3.3H_2O \xrightarrow{\text{Heat}} Al_2O_3 \;+\; 3H_2O$$

Hydrated aluminium oxide → Aluminium oxide

Stage 2: Separating aluminium from aluminium oxide by electrolysis

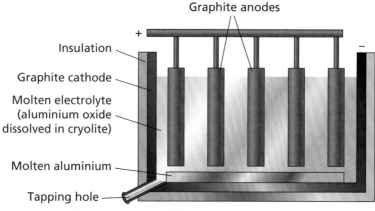

The extraction of aluminium metal from aluminium oxide by electrolysis

- In an aluminium smelter as shown, the aluminium oxide is mixed with molten cryolite (Na_3AlF_6) and aluminium fluoride (AlF_3) which lowers the melting point. A low voltage is used to avoid decomposing the electrolyte. Huge amounts of electricity are required for the electrolysis and this is why it is only carried out where cheap electricity is available. For this reason, it is not done in Ireland.
- Cathode($-$) reaction: $Al^{3+} \;+\; 3e^- \longrightarrow Al$
- Anode($+$) reaction: $2O^{2-} \longrightarrow O_2 \;+\; 4e^-$
  Overall reaction: $Al_2O_3 \longrightarrow 2Al \;+\; 1\frac{1}{2}O_2$
- Oxygen is produced at the anode. The graphite electrodes react with the oxygen and have to be replaced periodically.
- Uses of aluminium: window frames, drink cans.
- Recycling of aluminium is very cost effective as it is only a fraction of the cost of producing the same quantity of aluminium from bauxite.

Anodising aluminium

This is an electrolytic process where aluminium is coated with a thick layer of aluminium oxide. In the electrolysis the aluminium is the anode and inert graphite or platinum electrodes are used.

The electrolyte is dilute sulfuric acid. The reactions are:

- anode(+) electrode: $2Al + 3H_2O \longrightarrow Al_2O_3 + 6H^+ + 6e^-$

A coating of aluminium oxide forms on aluminium anode:

- cathode(−)electrode: $2H^+ + 2e^- \longrightarrow H_2$

Hydrogen gas formed at the cathode.

The oxide layer of anodised aluminium is porous which allows it to be dyed brown.

Manufacture of iron and steel

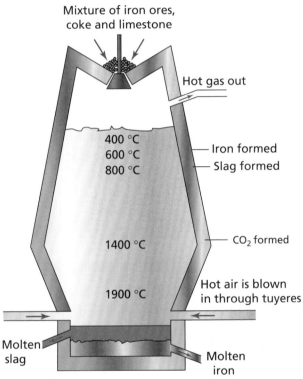

Blast furnace to extract iron metal from iron ore

The main ore in the production of iron is Haematite (Fe_2O_3).

- The extraction of iron metal is carried out in a blast furnace as shown in the diagram.
- The reaction mixture of haematite, coke and limestone are fed in at the top of the furnace.
- Hot air is blown into furnace and the main reaction occurring is:

$$Fe_2O_3 + 3C \longrightarrow 2Fe + 3CO$$

  Haematite   Coke   Iron   Carbon monoxide

The coke is a reducing agent here reducing iron(III) oxide to iron.

- The coke has two other functions:
  - (i) it acts as a fuel providing heat for the endothermic reaction above. The coke burns in hot air to produce carbon dioxide

  $$C + O_2 \longrightarrow CO_2$$

  This is an exothermic reaction and helps maintain the heat of the furnace.
  - (ii) it acts as a support for the materials in the furnace. Coke is a porous material and allows hot gases to flow upward through it and the hot molten iron can also trickle downward.

- The carbon monoxide formed in the main reaction above acts as the main reducing agent to convert the iron ore to iron metal:

  $$Fe_2O_3 + 3CO \longrightarrow 2Fe + 3CO_2$$

- The limestone is used to remove impurities of sand, SiO_2. The limestone decomposes first into lime and carbon dioxide as:

  $$CaCO_3 \longrightarrow CaO + CO_2$$

  Then the lime reacts with the sand to form 'slag' as:

  $$CaO + SiO_2 \longrightarrow CaSiO_3 \quad \text{(calcium silicate or 'slag')}.$$

  The slag is less dense than the molten iron and floats on top of it. The slag is removed at intervals and is used for road building.

- Uses of the cast iron: most of the pig iron or cast iron produced by the furnace is converted to steel but some is used for manhole covers and engine blocks.

Manufacture of steel

To convert pig iron from the furnace into steel:
- pure oxygen is blown through it to remove impurities such as carbon and sulfur forming carbon dioxide and sulfur dioxide gases
- measured amounts of different elements like tungsten and chromium are added to give steel of a particular quality.

Electric arc process of producing steel

An alternative method of manufacturing steel is to produce it from recycled scrap iron and steel. A special furnace called an electric arc furnace is used and the stages in production are:

- **Charging:** steel and scrap metal placed in furnace using an overhead crane.
- **Melting:** a huge electric current is passed between graphite electrodes close to the scrap. The high temperature produced by the arc (3500 °C) melts the scrap.

- **Sampling and refining:** a sample of the molten steel is removed from the furnace and analysed for different elements. Oxygen is blown into the furnace to remove excess carbon as carbon dioxide. Silicon is also oxidised to silicon dioxide.

Calcium oxide (lime) is then added to remove the silicon dioxide as slag:

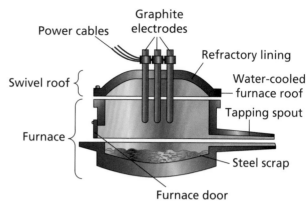

Electric arc process to manufacture steel

$$CaO \quad + \quad SiO_2 \quad \longrightarrow \quad CaSiO_3$$
(calcium silicate or 'slag').

The slag is less dense than the steel and therefore floats on top. The furnace is tilted to remove the slag.

- **Tapping:** the furnace is tilted forward and the molten steel is poured into ladles. Various other metals are now added to the steel to vary the properties of the steel as required.
- **Casting:** the molten steel is then poured into the top of a casting machine where it is cooled into a mould using water. The steel is then cut into the required lengths.
- **Environmental aspects:** air pollution must be prevented by:
  - (i) 'scrubbing' SO_2 using limestone
  - (ii) removing dust electostatically.

Also the slag removed during the process is used in road building.

Uses of steel

It is used in the manufacture of (i) car bodies (ii) bridges and buildings.